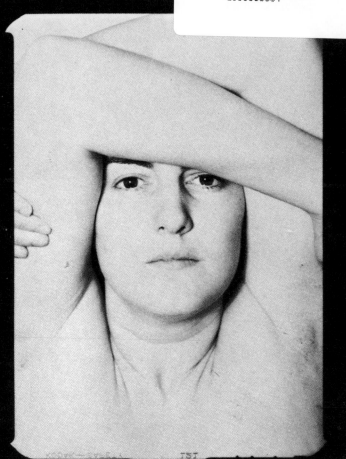

LONGMAN IMPRINT BOOKS

Women

a collection of writings by women about women,
with a sequence of photographs

compiled and edited by
Maura Healy

Longman

LONGMAN GROUP UK LIMITED
Longman House
Burnt Mill, Harlow, Essex CM20 2JE, England and
Associated Companies throughout the world.

This edition first published 1984
Fourth impression 1988
ISBN 0 582 22104 8

Set in 10/11 pt Baskerville, Linotron 202

Produced by Longman Singapore Publishers Pte Ltd
Printed in Singapore

Dedication

For Mary and Vincent, with thanks

Contents

Cover painting is *After the Meeting* by Cecilia Beaux
(1855–1942)

Frontispiece: *Eleanor, Chicago* 1949 by Harry Callahan

An Introductory Note

The last ten years have seen a remarkable growth in the publication of literature by and about women. My task has been to select from that rich profusion, material appropriate for senior students in secondary schools and colleges.

All along I have been choosing this story rather than that, rather than another. As I read more and more of the available literature and tried out stories and poems in my own classes, certain guiding principles became clear.

The briefest of glimpse at examination syllabi and of many English stock cupboards reveals a startling discrepancy. Male authors and themes predominate. There was a need, then, to legitimize the female experience as a focus of study. Further, there was a need to offer descriptions of that experience which extended beyond the domestic and caring roles women too often play in texts used in schools.

The material I chose had to stand by itself in terms of literary merit, but it should offer a more balanced reflection of the world. It should pose questions and stimulate discussion and thought about our world and the task of the writer in communicating a perception of it.

The material also had to cover a range of perceptions and experiences.

The present selection is roughly chronological, starting as it does with childhood and working its way through loving and learning, befriending, parenting, working and dying.

Much is omitted on the way. The selection uses mainly English and American material. Its concern with items of a predominantly literary genre leaves no space for some of the excellent non-fiction biographical material which gives a direct voice to the experience of working-class women, although many of the stories explore those experiences.

The material had to span centuries. It was important that the voice of women was seen to be no new sound although some of

the writers had been awaiting rediscovery and acknowledge-
ment of their worth in the new emergence of women's fiction.

The material had to offer a range of responses to the role of
women in society. It was hoped that the juxtaposition of, say
"The Telephone Call" and "Reclamation" should provide more
dialogue on that role than a single statement could offer.

Finally the material had to be accessible to students female
and male. It should speak for itself. The discussion points and
suggestions for writing should merely aid students in bringing
their own experience, feelings and skills into contact with the
voice of the writer.

It so happened that each item is written by a woman. Initially
that was not a criterion for selection but in the search for an
authentic voice, the choice of female writers made itself.

Maura Healy

Margaret Atwood

Lady Oracle: The Butterfly Frolic

I loved dancing school. I was even quite good at the actual dancing, although Miss Flegg sometimes rapped her classroom pointer sharply on the floor and said, "Joan dear, I wish you would stop thumping." Like most little girls of that time I idealized ballet dancers, it was something girls could do, and I used to press my short piggy nose up against jewelry store windows and goggle at the china music-box figurines of shiny ladies in brittle pink skirts, with roses on their hard ceramic heads, and imagine myself leaping through the air, lifted by a thin man in black tights, light as a kite and wearing a modified doily, my hair full of rhinestones and glittering like hope. I worked hard at the classes, I concentrated, and I even used to practise at home, wrapping myself in a discarded lace bathroom curtain I had begged from my mother as she was about to stuff it into the garbage can. She washed it first though; she didn't like dirt. I longed for a pair of satin toe shoes, but we were too young, Miss Flegg explained, the bones in our feet had not hardened. So I had to settle for black slippers with an unromantic elastic over the instep.

Miss Flegg was an inventive woman; I suppose these days she would be called creative. She didn't have much scope for her inventiveness in the teaching of elementary steps to young children, which was largely a matter of drill, but she let herself go on the annual spring recital. The recital was mostly to impress the parents, but it was also to impress the little girls themselves so they would ask to be allowed to take lessons the next year.

Miss Flegg choreographed the entire program. She also constructed the sets and props, and she designed the costumes and handed out patterns and instructions to the mothers, who were supposed to sew them. My mother disliked sewing but for this event she buckled down and cut and pinned just like all the other mothers. Maybe she hadn't given up on me after all, maybe she was still making an effort.

Miss Flegg organized the recital into age groups, which corresponded to her dancing classes. There were five of them: Teenies, Tallers, Tensies, Tweeners and Teeners. Underneath her spiny exterior, the long bony hands, the hair wrenched into a bun, and the spidery eyebrows, done, I realized later, with a pencil, she had a layer of sentimentality, which set the tone for her inventions.

I was a Teenie, which was in itself a contradiction in terms, for as well as being heavier than everyone else in the class I had begun to be taller. But I didn't mind, I didn't even notice, for I was becoming more wildly excited about the recital every day. I practised for hours in the basement, the only place I was allowed to do it after I had accidentally knocked over and broken my mother's white-and-gold living-room lamp in the shape of a pineapple, one of a set. I twirled beside the washing machine, humming the dance music in my head, I curtseyed to the furnace (which in those days still burned coal), I swayed in and out between the sheets drying double-folded on the line, and when I was exhausted I climbed the cellar stairs, out of breath and covered with coal dust, to be confronted by my mother with her mouth full of pins. After I'd been scrubbed I would be stood on a chair and told to turn around slowly. I could barely hold still even to have my costumes tried on.

My mother's impatience was almost equal to my own, though it was of another sort. She may have started to regret sending me to dancing school. For one thing, I wasn't getting any slimmer; for another, I now made twice as much noise as I had at first, especially when I rehearsed my tap number in my patent leather shoes with metal tips toe and heel, on the hardwood of the hall floor, which I had been ordered not to do; and for another, she was having trouble with the costumes. She'd followed the instructions, but she couldn't get them to look right.

There were three of them, for the Teenies were doing three numbers: "Tulip Time," a Dutch ballet routine for which we had to line up with partners and move our arms up and down to simulate windmills; "Anchors Aweigh," a tap dance with quick turns and salutes (this was soon after the end of the war and military motifs were still in vogue); and "The Butterfly Frolic," a graceful number whose delicate flittings were more

like my idea of what dancing should be. It was my favorite, and it had my favorite costume too. This featured a gauzy skirt, short, like a real ballerina's, a tight bodice with shoulder straps, a headpiece with spangled insect antennae, and a pair of colored cellophane wings with coathanger frames, supplied by Miss Flegg. The wings were what I really longed for but we weren't allowed to put them on until the day itself, for fear of breakage.

But it was this costume that was bothering my mother. The others were easier: the Dutch outfit was a long full skirt with a black bodice and white sleeves, and I was the rear partner anyway. The "Anchors Aweigh" number had middy dresses with naval braid trim, and this was all right too since they were high-necked, longsleeved and loose around the waist. I was in the back row because of my height; I hadn't been picked as one of the three stars, all with Shirley Temple curls, who were doing solos on drums made out of cheese crates. But I didn't mind that much: I had my eye on the chief butterfly spot. There was a duet with the only boy in the class; his name was Roger, I was slightly in love with him. I hoped the girl who was supposed to do it would get sick and they would have to call me in. I'd memorized her part as well as my own, more or less.

I stood on the chair and my mother stuck pins into me and sighed; then she told me to turn around slowly, and she frowned and stuck in more pins. The problem was fairly simple: in the short pink skirt, with my waist, arms and legs exposed, I was grotesque. I am reconstructing this from the point of view of an adult, an anxious, prudish adult like my mother or Miss Flegg; but with my jiggly thighs and the bulges of fat where breasts would later be and my plump upper arms and floppy waist, I must have looked obscene, senile almost, indecent; it must have been like watching a decaying stripper. I was the kind of child, they would have thought back then in the early months of 1949, who should not be seen in public with so little clothing on. No wonder I fell in love with the nineteenth century: back then, according to the dirty postcards of the time, flesh was a virtue.

My mother struggled with the costume, lengthening it, adding another layer of gauze to conceal the outlines, padding the bodice; but it was no use. Even I was a little taken aback when she finally allowed me to inspect myself in the three-sided mirror over her vanity table. Although I was too young to be much bothered by my size, it wasn't quite the effect I wanted. I did not look like a butterfly. But I knew the addition of the wings would make all the difference. I was hoping for magic transformations, even then.

The dress rehearsal was in the afternoon, the recital the same evening. They were so close together because the recital was to be held, not in the room over the butcher shop, which would have been too cramped, but in a public school auditorium, rented for a single Saturday. My mother went with me, carrying my costumes in a cardboard dress box. The stage was cramped and hollow-sounding but was redeemed by velvet curtains, soft purple ones; I felt them at the first opportunity. The space behind it was vibrating with excitement. A lot of the mothers were there. Some of them had volunteered to do makeup and were painting the faces of theirs and other people's daughters, the mouths with dark-red lipstick, the eyelashes with black mascara which stiffened them into spikes. The finished and costumed girls were standing against the wall so as not to damage themselves, inert as temple sacrifices. The bigger pupils were strolling about and chatting; it wasn't as important to them, they had done it before, and their numbers were to be rehearsed later.

"Tulip Time" and "Anchors Aweigh" went off without a hitch. We changed costumes backstage, in a tangle of arms and legs, giggling nervously and doing up each other's hooks and zippers. There was a crowd around the single mirror. The Tallers, who were alternating with us, did their number, "Kitty Kat Kapers," while Miss Flegg stood in the wings, evaluating, waving time with her pointer, and occasionally shouting. She was wrought up. As I was putting on my butterfly costume, I saw my mother standing beside her.

She was supposed to be out in the front row where I'd left her, sitting on a folding chair, her gloves in her lap, smoking and jiggling one of her feet in its high-heeled open-toed shoe, but now she was talking with Miss Flegg. Miss Flegg looked over at me; then she walked over, followed by my mother. She stood gazing down at me, her lips pressed together.

"I see what you mean," she said to my mother. When resenting this scene later on, I always felt that if my mother hadn't interfered Miss Flegg would have noticed nothing, but this is probably not true. What she was seeing, what they were both seeing, was her gay, her artistic, her *spiritual* "Butterfly Frolic" being reduced to something laughable and unseemly by the presence of a fat little girl who was more like a giant caterpillar than a butterfly, more like a white grub if you were really going to be accurate.

Miss Flegg could not have stood this. For her, the final effect was everything. She wished to be complimented on it, and whole-heartedly, not with pity or suppressed smiles, I sympathize with her now, although I couldn't then. Anyway, her inventiveness didn't desert her. She leaned down, placed her hand on my round bare shoulder, and drew me over to a corner. There she knelt down and gazed with her forceful black eyes into mine. Her blurred eyebrows rose and fell.

"Joan, dear," she said, "how would you like to be something special?"

I smiled at her uncertainly.

"Would you do something for me, dear?" she said, warmly.

I nodded. I liked to help.

"I've decided to change the dance a little," she said. "I've decided to add a new part to it; and because you're the brightest girl in the class, I've chosen you to be the special, new person. Do you think you can do that, dear?"

I had seen enough of her to know that this kindness was suspect, but I fell for it anyway. I nodded emphatically, thrilled to have been selected. Maybe I'd been picked to do the butterfly duet with Roger, maybe I would get bigger, more important wings. I was eager.

"Good," said Miss Flegg, clamping her hand on my arm. "Now come and hop into your new costume."

"What am I going to be?" I asked as she led me away.

"A mothball, dear," she answered serenely, as if this were the most natural thing in the world.

Her inventive mind; and possibly earlier experiences, had given her a fundamental rule for dealing with situations like this: if you're going to be made to look ridiculous and there's no way out of it, you may as well pretend you meant to. I didn't learn this rule till much later, not consciously. I was wounded, desolated in fact, when it turned out that Miss Flegg wanted me to remove my cloudy skirt and spangles and put on one of the white teddy-bear costumes the Tensies were using for their number, "Teddy Bears' Picnic." She also wanted me to hang around my neck a large sign that said MOTHBALL, "So they'll all understand, dear, what you're supposed to be." She herself would make the sign for me, in the interval between the rehearsal and the performance.

"Can I wear my wings?" I asked. It was beginning to seep through to me, the monstrousness of the renunciation she was asking me to make.

"Now, who ever heard of a mothball with wings?" she said in what was supposed to be a jocular but practical manner.

Her idea was that once the butterflies had finished their cavorting, I would lumber in among them in the white suit and the sign, and the butterflies would be coached to scatter. It would be cute, she told me.

"I liked the dance the way it was," I said tentatively. "I want it to be the way it was." I was on the verge of crying; probably I had already begun.

Miss Flegg's manner changed. She put her face down close to mine so I could see the wrinkles around her eyes up close and smell the sour toothpaste smell of her mouth, and said, slowly and distinctly, "You'll do as I say or you won't be in the dance at all. Do you understand?"

Being left out altogether was too much for me. I capitulated, but I paid for it. I had to stand in the mothball suit with Miss Flegg's hand on my shoulder while she explained to the other Teenies, sylphlike in their wispy skirts and shining wings, about the change in plans and my new, starring role. They looked at me, scorn on their painted lips; they were not taken in.

I went home with my mother, refusing to speak to her because she had betrayed me. It was snowing lightly, though it was April, and I was glad because she had on her white open-toed shoes and her feet would get wet. I went into the bathroom and locked the door so she couldn't get at me; then I wept uncontrollably, lying on the floor with my face against the fluffy pink bath mat. Afterwards I pulled the laundry hamper over so I could stand on it and look into the bathroom mirror. My made-up face had run, there were black streaks down my cheeks like sooty tears and my purple mouth was smudged and swollen. What was the matter with me? It wasn't that I couldn't dance.

My mother pleaded briefly with me through the locked bathroom door, then she threatened. I came out, but I wouldn't eat any dinner: someone besides me would have to suffer. My mother wiped the makeup off my face with Pond's Cold Cream, scolding me because it would have to be done over, and we set out again for the auditorium. (Where was my father? He wasn't there.)

I had to stand enviously in the wings, red-faced and steaming in the hated suit, listening to the preliminary coughs and the scraping of folding chairs, then watching while the butterflies tinkled through the movements I myself had memorized, I was sure, better than any of them. The worst thing was that I still didn't understand quite why this was being done to me, this humiliation disguised as a privilege.

At the right moment Miss Flegg gave me a shove and I lurched onto the stage, trying to look, as she had instructed me, as much like a mothball as possible. Then I danced. There were no steps to my dance, as I hadn't been taught any, so I made it up as I went along. I swung my arms, I bumped into the butterflies, I spun in circles and stamped my feet as hard as I could on the boards of the flimsy stage, until it shook. I threw myself into the part, it was a dance of rage and destruction, tears rolled down my cheeks behind the fur, the butterflies would die; my feet hurt for days afterwards. "This isn't me," I kept saying to myself, "they're making me do it"; yet even though I was concealed in the teddy-bear suit, which flopped about me and made me sweat, I felt naked and exposed, as if this ridiculous dance was the truth about me and everyone could see it.

The butterflies scampered away on cue and much to my surprise I was left in the center of the stage, facing an audience that was not only laughing but applauding vigorously. Even when the beauties, the tiny thin ones, trooped back for their curtsey, the laughter and clapping went on, and several people, who must have been fathers rather than mothers, shouted "Bravo mothball". It puzzled me that some of them seemed to like my ugly, bulky suit better than the pretty ones of the others.

After the recital Miss Flegg was congratulated on her priceless touch with the mothball. Even my mother appeared pleased. "You did fine," she said, but I still cried that night over my thwarted wings. I would never get a chance to use them now, since I had decided already that much as I loved dancing school I was not going back to it in the fall. It's true I had received more individual attention than the others, but I wasn't sure it was a kind I liked. Besides, who would think of marrying a mothball? A question my mother put to me often, later, in other forms.

Carol Schachter

Miss Kindergarten America

Miss Kindergarten America of 1984 hitched up her garters and teetered back to her hotel room overlooking the boardwalk. She was a very small beauty queen and it had been a tiring day, the most exciting day of her whole life. She had done it! She had won the title and next year, Mommy promised, she could enter the preliminaries for the Miss Pre-Sub-Teen America pageant. Oh, Mommy was so happy!

As soon as she closed her door, she stepped out of her high heels and ripped off her girdle. Gee, that felt good! Standing all afternoon at the Coketail press party had been awful.

She undressed and stood at the mirror, looking at her figure. When she had reached the semifinals, she had stopped eating cookies and ice cream and started smoking. Then she had really lost a lot of weight. Daddy called it "baby fat" and said leave it alone, but Mommy said after all, the child is five and it's about time she thought about her shape. (She didn't really like the taste of cigarettes too much, but ever since the sixth graders got their own smoking lounge at school, all the younger kids sneaked a few drags at recess, hiding under the slide. And then it got to be a habit.)

She carefully removed her makeup with Big Idea Moisturizing Cleanser, slapped on some Big Idea Skin Freshener and Big Idea Hormone Night Cream. She considered not setting her hair but knew it was hopeless. Her perm was growing out and this morning Kenneth had teased her hair so much (to make it look natural), she knew it would collapse overnight. Maybe she'd run in for a comb-out after breakfast.

A half hour later all the rollers were in place and she rubbed her aching arms. She laid out her dress for the next day's festivities – a stunning little nothing from Saks, all shape and line. She'd be able to wear it to the PTA first-grade dancing classes next year, so $89.95 wasn't really expensive. Even Mommy had said it was a thoughtful investment.

She set her clock-TV for 6:30 and tucked in her doll family for the night. Santa Claus had brought her the whole set last Christmas. It came in a big box with three double beds and a new educational toy, "The Mating Game". There was Grandma Barbie and Grandpa Ken and Daughter Sally and Son-in-Law Rob and their daughter Lolly and her boyfriend Tom. Sally came equipped with snap-on bosoms and snap-on tummies and a yummy wardrobe of maternity clothes so you could pretend she was in all different months.

She got under the covers and lay on her side, her arms and legs curled up under her chin. The rollers hurt like anything. She thought how nice it would be to go home and see Daddy. She really hadn't spent much time with him since Tabitha Carleton's fifth-birthday coming-out party. Ever since that night, she'd been busy working for the title.

The party had been lots of fun but, gee, what a mess after those grade boys crashed it and spiked all the Cokes. All those broken windows and doll furniture thrown all over the beach. ... But still, it was the publicity that had started her on the road to the crown. Mommy took her straight to the modelling agency in New York, and she hadn't been so busy since she was three and a cheerleader for the Little Punks Tiny Football League. Now here she was, at last, Miss Kindergarten America.

She tried and tried to find a comfortable position but something didn't feel quite right. Something was missing. Then she remembered and ran over to the closet. Oh good! No one had found the bag she had stuffed behind her mink stole. She went back to bed. With her mangy teddy bear, an old plush elephant, and a somewhat soiled rag doll cuddled fiercely in her arms, she fell sound asleep.

Toni Morrison

The Coming of Maureen Peal

My daddy's face is a study. Winter moves into it and presides there. His eyes become a cliff of snow threatening to avalanche; his eyebrows bend like black limbs of leafless trees. His skin takes on the pale, cheerless yellow of winter sun; for a jaw he has the edges of a snowbound field dotted with stubble; his high forehead is the frozen sweep of the Erie, hiding currents of gelid thoughts that eddy in darkness. Wolf killer turned hawk fighter, he worked night and day to keep one from the door and the other from under the windowsills. A Vulcan guarding the flames, he gives us instructions about which doors to keep closed or opened for proper distribution of heat, lays kindling by, discusses qualities of coal, and teaches us how to rake, feed, and bank the fire. And he will not unrazor his lips until spring.

Winter tightened our heads with a band of cold and melted our eyes. We put pepper in the feet of our stockings, Vaseline on our faces, and stared through dark icebox mornings at four stewed prunes, slippery lumps of oatmeal, and cocoa with a roof of skin.

But mostly we waited for spring, when there could be gardens.

By the time this winter had stiffened itself into a hateful knot that nothing could loosen, something did loosen it, or rather someone. A someone who splintered the knot into silver threads that tangled us, netted us, made us long for the dull chafe of the previous boredom.

This disrupter of seasons was a new girl in school named Maureen Peal. A high-yellow dream child with long brown hair braided into two lynch ropes that hung down her back. She was rich, at least by our standards, as rich as the richest of the white girls, swaddled in comfort and care. The quality of her clothes threatened to derange Frieda and me. Patent-leather shoes with buckles, a cheaper version of which we got only at Easter and which had disintegrated by the end of May. Fluffy sweaters the color of lemon drops tucked into skirts with pleats so orderly they astounded us. Brightly colored knee socks with white borders, a brown velvet coat trimmed in white rabbit fur, and a matching muff. There was a hint of spring in her sloe green eyes, something summery in her complexion, and a rich autumn ripeness in her walk.

She enchanted the entire school. When teachers called on her, they smiled encouragingly. Black boys didn't trip her in the halls; white boys didn't stone her, white girls didn't suck their teeth when she was assigned to be their work partners; black girls stepped aside when she wanted to use the sink in the girls' toilet, and their eyes genuflected under sliding lids. She never had to search for anybody to eat with in the cafeteria – they flocked to the table of her choice, where she opened fastidious lunches, shaming our jelly-stained bread with egg-salad sandwiches cut into four dainty squares, pink-frosted cupcakes, sticks of celery and carrots, proud, dark apples. She even bought and liked white milk.

Frieda and I were bemused, irritated, and fascinated by her. We looked hard for flaws to restore our equilibrium, but had to be content at first with uglying up her name, changing Maureen Peal to Meringue Pie. Later a minor epiphany was ours when we discovered that she had a dog tooth – a charming one to be sure – but a dog tooth nonetheless. And when we found out that she had been born with six fingers on each hand and that there was a little bump where each extra one had been removed, we smiled. They were small triumphs, but we took what we could get – snickering behind her back and calling her Six-finger-dog-tooth-meringue-pie. But we had to do it alone, for none of the other girls would co-operate with our hostility. They adored her.

When she was assigned a locker next to mine, I could indulge my jealousy four times a day. My sister and I both suspected that we were secretly prepared to be her friend, if she would let us, but I knew it would be a dangerous friendship, for when my eye traced the white border patterns of those Kelly-green knee socks, and felt the pull and slack of my brown stockings, I wanted to kick her. And when I thought of the unearned haughtiness in her eyes, I plotted accidental slammings of locker doors on her hand.

As locker friends, however, we got to know each other a little, and I was even able to hold a sensible conversation with her without visualizing her fall off a cliff, or giggling my way into what I thought was a clever insult.

One day, while I waited at the locker for Frieda, she joined me.

"Hi."

"Hi."

"Waiting for your sister?"

"Uh-huh."

"Which way do you go home?"

"Down Twenty-first Street to Broadway."

"Why don't you go down Twenty-second Street?"

" 'Cause I live on Twenty-first Street."

"Oh. I can walk that way, I guess. Partly, anyway."

"Free country."

Frieda came toward us, her brown stockings straining at the knees because she had tucked the toe under to hide a hole in the foot.

"Maureen's gonna walk part way with us."

Frieda and I exchanged glances, her eyes begging my restraint, mine promising nothing.

It was a false spring day, which, like Maureen, had pierced the shell of a deadening winter. There were puddles, mud, and an inviting warmth that deluded us. The kind of day on which we draped our coats over our heads, left our galoshes in school, and came down with croup the following day. We always responded to the slightest change in weather, the most minute shifts in time of day. Long before seeds were stirring, Frieda and I were scuffing and poking at the earth, swallowing air, drinking rain . . .

As we emerged from the school with Maureen, we began to molt immediately. We put our head scarves in our coat pockets, and our coats on our heads. I was wondering how to maneuver Maureen's fur muff into a gutter when a commotion in the playground distracted us. A group of boys was circling and holding at bay a victim, Pecola Breedlove.

Bay Boy, Woodrow Cain, Buddy Wilson, Junie Bug – like a necklace of semiprecious stones they surrounded her. Heady with the smell of their own musk, thrilled by the easy power of a majority, they gaily harassed her.

"Black e mo. Black e mo. Yadaddsleepsnekked. Black e mo black e mo ya dadd sleeps nekked. Black e mo. . ."

They had extemporized a verse made up of two insults about

matters over which the victim had no control; the color of her skin and speculations on the sleeping habits of an adult, wildly fitting in its incoherence. That they themselves were black, or that their own father had similarly relaxed habits was irrelevant. It was their contempt for their own blackness that gave the first insult its teeth. They seemed to have taken all of their smoothly cultivated ignorance, their exquisitely learned self-hatred, their elaborately designed hopelessness and sucked it all up into a fiery cone of scorn that had burned for ages in the hollows of their minds – cooled – and spilled over lips of outrage, consuming whatever was in its path. They danced a macabre ballet around the victim, whom, for their own sake, they were prepared to sacrifice to the flaming pit.

> Black e mo Black e mo Ya daddy sleeps nekked.
> Stch ta ta stch ta ta
> stach ta ta ta ta ta

Pecola edged around the circle crying. She had dropped her notebook, and covered her eyes with her hands.

We watched, afraid they might notice us and turn their energies our way. Then Frieda, with set lips and Mama's eyes, snatched her coat from her head and threw it on the ground. She ran toward them and brought her books down on Woodrow Cain's head. The circle broke. Woodrow Cain grabbed his head.

"Hey, girl!"

"You cut that out, you hear?" I had never heard Frieda's voice so loud and clear.

Maybe because Frieda was taller than he was, maybe because he saw her eyes, maybe because he had lost interest in the game, or maybe because he had a crush on Frieda, in any case Woodrow looked frightened just long enough to give her more courage.

"Leave her 'lone, or I'm gone tell everybody what you did!"

Woodrow did not answer; he just walled his eyes.

Bay Boy piped up, "Go on, gal. Ain't nobody bothering you."

"You shut up, Bullet Head." I had found my tongue.

"Who you calling Bullet Head?"

"I'm calling you Bullet Head, Bullet Head."

Frieda took Pecola's hand. "Come on."

"You want a fat lip?" Bay Boy drew back his fist at me.

"Yeah. Gimme one of yours."

"You gone get one."

Maureen appeared at my elbow, and the boys seemed reluctant to continue under her springtime eyes so wide with interest. They buckled in confusion, not willing to beat up three girls under her watchful gaze. So they listened to a budding male instinct that told them to pretend we were unworthy of their attention.

"Come on, man."

"Yeah. Come on. We ain't got time to fool with them."

Grumbling a few disinterested epithets, they moved away.

I picked up Pecola's notebook and Frieda's coat, and the four of us left the playground.

"Old Bullet Head, he's always picking on girls."

Frieda agreed with me. "Miss Forrester said he was incorrigival."

"Really?" I didn't know what that meant, but it had enough of a doom sound in it to be true of Bay Boy.

While Frieda and I clucked on about the near fight, Maureen, suddenly animated, put her velvet-sleeved arm through Pecola's and began to behave as though they were the closest of friends.

"I just moved here. My name is Maureen Peal. What's yours?"

"Pecola."

"Pecola? Wasn't that the name of the girl in *Imitation of Life*?"

"I don't know. What is that?"

"The picture show, you know. Where this mulatto girl hates her mother 'cause she is black and ugly but then cries at the funeral. It was real sad. Everybody cries in it. Claudette Colbert too."

"Oh." Pecola's voice was no more than a sigh.

"Anyway, her name was Pecola too. She was so pretty. When it comes back, I'm going to see it again. My mother has seen it four times."

Frieda and I walked behind them, surprised at Maureen's friendliness to Pecola, but pleased. Maybe she wasn't so bad, after all. Frieda had put her coat back on her head, and the two of us, so draped, trotted along enjoying the warm breeze and Frieda's heroics.

"You're in my gym class, aren't you?" Maureen asked Pecola.

"Yes."

"Miss Erkmeister's legs sure are bow. I bet she thinks they're cute. How come she gets to wear real shorts, and we have to

15

wear those old bloomers? I want to die every time I put them on."

Pecola smiled but did not look at Maureen.

"Hey." Maureen stopped short. "There's an Isaley's. Want some ice cream? I have money."

She unzipped a hidden pocket in her muff and pulled out a multifolded dollar bill. I forgave her those knee socks.

"My uncle sued Isaley's," Maureen said to the three of us. "He sued the Isaley's in Akron. They said he was disorderly and that that was why they wouldn't serve him, but a friend of his, a policeman, came in and beared the witness, so the suit went through."

"What's a suit?"

"It's when you can beat them up if you want to and won't anybody do nothing. Our family does it all the time. We believe in suits."

At the entrance to Isaley's, Maureen turned to Frieda and me, asking, "You all going to buy some ice cream?"

We looked at each other. "No," Frieda said.

Maureen disappeared into the store with Pecola.

Frieda looked placidly down the street; I opened my mouth, but quickly closed it. It was extremely important that the world not know that I fully expected Maureen to buy us some ice cream, that for the past 120 seconds I had been selecting the flavor, that I had begun to like Maureen, and that neither of us had a penny.

We supposed Maureen was being nice to Pecola because of the boys, and were embarrassed to be caught – even by each other – thinking that she would treat us, or that we deserved it as much as Pecola did.

The girls came out. Pecola with two dips of orange-pineapple, Maureen with black raspberry.

"You should have got some," she said. "They had all kinds. Don't eat down to the tip of the cone," she advised Pecola.

"Why?"

"Because there's a fly in there."

"How you know?"

"Oh, not really. A girl told me she found one in the bottom of hers once, and ever since then she throws that part away."

"Oh."

We passed the Dreamland Theater, and Betty Grable smiled down at us.

"Don't you just love her?" Maureen asked.

"Uh-huh," said Pecola.

I differed. "Hedy Lamarr is better."

Maureen agreed. "Ooooo yes. My mother told me that a girl named Audrey, she went to the beauty parlor where we lived before, and asked the lady to fix her hair like Hedy Lamarr's, and the lady said, 'Yeah, when you grow some hair like Hedy Lamarr's.' " She laughed long and sweet.

"Sounds crazy," said Frieda.

"She sure is. Do you know she doesn't even menstrate yet, and she's sixteen. Do you, yet?"

"Yes." Pecola glanced at us.

"So do I." Maureen made no attempt to disguise her pride. "Two months ago I started. My girl friend in Toledo, where we lived before, said when she started she was scared to death. Thought she had killed herself."

"Do you know what it's for?" Pecola asked the question as though hoping to provide the answer herself.

"For babies." Maureen raised two pencil-stroke eyebrows at the obviousness of the question. "Babies need blood when they are inside you, and if you are having a baby, then you don't menstrate. But when you're not having a baby, then you don't have to save the blood, so it comes out."

"How do babies get the blood?" asked Pecola.

"Through the like-line. You know. Where your belly button is. That is where the like-line grows from and pumps the blood to the baby."

"Well, if the belly buttons are to grow like-lines to give the baby blood, and only girls have babies, how come boys have belly buttons?"

Maureen hesitated. "I don't know," she admitted. "But boys have all sorts of things they don't need." Her tinkling laughter was somehow stronger than our nervous ones. She curled her tongue around the edge of the cone, scooping up a dollop of purple that made my eyes water. We were waiting for a stop light to change. Maureen kept scooping the ice cream from around the cone's edge with her tongue; she didn't bite the edge as I would have done. Her tongue circled the cone. Pecola had finished hers; Maureen evidently liked her things to last. While I was thinking about her ice cream, she must have been thinking about her last remark, for she said to Pecola, "Did you ever see a naked man?"

17

Pecola blinked, then looked away. "No. Where would I see a naked man?"

"I don't know. I just asked."

"I wouldn't even look at him, even if I did see him. That's dirty. Who wants to see a naked man?" Pecola was agitated, "Nobody's father would be naked in front of his own daughter. Not unless he was dirty too."

"I didn't say 'father'. I just said 'a naked man'."

"Well . . ."

"How come you said 'father'?" Maureen wanted to know.

"Who else would she see, dog tooth?" I was glad to have a chance to show anger. Not only because of the ice cream, but because we had seen our own father naked and didn't care to be reminded of it and feel the shame brought on by the absence of shame. He had been walking down the hall from the bathroom into his bedroom and passed the open door of our room. We had lain there wide-eyed. He stopped and looked in, trying to see in the dark room whether we were really asleep – or was it his imagination that opened eyes were looking at him? Apparently he convinced himself that we were sleeping. He moved away, confident that his little girls would not lie open-eyed like that, staring, staring. When he had moved on, the dark took only him away, not his nakedness. That stayed in the room with us. Friendly-like.

"I'm not talking to you," said Maureen. "Besides, I don't care if she sees her father naked. She can look at him all day if she wants to. Who cares?"

"You do," said Frieda. "That's all you talk about."

"It is not."

"It is so. Boys, babies, and somebody's naked daddy. You must be boy-crazy."

"You better be quiet."

"Who's gonna make me?" Frieda put her hand on her hip and jutted her face toward Maureen.

"You all ready made. Mammy made."

"You stop talking about my mama."

"Well, you stop talking about my daddy."

"Who said anything about your old daddy?"

"You did."

"Well, you started it."

"I wasn't even talking to you. I was talking to Pecola."

"Yeah. About seeing her naked daddy."

"So what if she did see him?"

Pecola shouted, "I never saw my daddy naked. Never."

"You did too," Maureen snapped, "Bay Boy said so."

"I did not."

"You did."

"I did not."

"Did. Your own daddy, too!"

Pecola tucked her head in – a funny, sad, helpless movement. A kind of hunching of the shoulders, pulling in of the neck, as though she wanted to cover her ears.

"You stop talking about her daddy," I said.

"What do I care about her old black daddy?" asked Maureen.

"Black? Who you calling black?"

"You."

"You think you so cute!" I swung at her and missed, hitting Pecola in the face. Furious at my clumsiness, I threw my notebook at her, but it caught her in the small of her velvet back, for she had turned and was flying across the street against traffic.

Safe on the other side, she screamed at us, "I *am* cute! And you ugly! Black and ugly black e mos. I *am* cute!"

She ran down the street, the green knee socks making her legs look like wild dandelion stems that had somehow lost their heads. The weight of her remark stunned us, and it was a second or two before Frieda and I collected ourselves enough to shout, "Six-finger-dog-tooth-meringue-pie!" We chanted this most powerful of our arsenal of insults as long as we could see the green stems and rabbit fur.

Grown people frowned at the three girls on the curbside, two with their coats draped over their heads, the collars framing the eyebrows like nuns' habits, black garters showing where they bit the tops of brown stockings that barely covered the knees, angry faces knotted like dark cauliflowers.

Pecola stood a little apart from us, her eyes hinged in the direction in which Maureen had fled. She seemed to fold into herself, like a pleated wing. Her pain antagonized me. I wanted to open her up, crisp her edges, ram a stick down that hunched and curving spine, force her to stand erect and spit the misery out on the streets. But she held it in where it could lap up into her eyes. Frieda snatched her coat from her head. "Come on, Claudia. 'Bye, Pecola."

We walked quickly at first, and then slower, pausing every now and then to fasten garters, tie shoelaces, scratch, or examine old scars. We were sinking under the wisdom, accuracy, and relevance of Maureen's last words. If she was cute – and if anything could be believed, she *was* – then we were not. And what did that mean? We were lesser. Nicer, brighter, but still lesser. Dolls we could destroy, but we could not destroy the honey voices of parents and aunts, the obedience in the eyes of our peers, the slippery light in the eyes of our teachers when they encountered the Maureen Peals of the world. What was the secret? What did we lack? Why was it important? And so what? Guileless and without vanity, we were still in love with ourselves then. We felt comfortable in our skins, enjoyed the news that our senses released to us, admired our dirt, cultivated our scars, and could not comprehend this unworthiness. Jealousy we understood and thought natural – a desire to have what somebody else had; but envy was a strange, new feeling for us. And all the time we knew that Maureen Peal was not the Enemy and not worthy of such intense hatred. The *Thing* to fear was the *Thing* that made *her* beautiful, and not us.

Christine Purkis

The Kiss

I'd idolized Bill Taylor for months. It was a secret and unde-
clared passion and began in a ballroom dancing class in the old
church hall.

I saw him, leaning against the window frame, smoking,
laughing with the other boys. He had blue eyes and curly fair
hair which he had dampened and brushed back in the manner
of the day so the curls rippled over his head like waves.

He didn't choose me to be his partner of course, and my
friend Anne and I ended up together again and arguing as to
who was going to be the man. Once I brushed against him as
I was being pushed blind into a complicated spin-turn by Anne.
He apologised and so did I. He had a green cord jacket on.

He never came to another class but each week was exciting
just anticipating him being there and the disappointment died
as the hope for the next week was born.

Then – there was to be a dance in St Aloysius Hall, tickets
in aid of the new Scout den. It was arranged by the local Rover
group and Bill Taylor was a Rover. He'd be bound to be there.

I put on my best blue check dress with the velvet covered
buttons and trim round the collar, and borrowed my sister's
blue sheer stockings with seams, though my suspender belt cut
deeply and painfully into my hips. I also borrowed her makeup and drew little smudgy grey lines on my eyelids and
mascara'd my eyelashes until my eyes watered.

The dance followed the usual pattern. For the first hour we,
the girls, stood in the hall, trembling with excitement, at one
end, with all the boys at the other and a few mums and dads
or elder brothers and sisters dancing in the space between.

Boredom, then depression followed on. The evening was
nearly over and Anne and I had only danced with each other
and there'd been no sign of Bill Taylor. She stared gloomily one
way and I the other, watching the couples twirl and spin.

"Do you want a coke?" she asked me.

"Yeh – all this dancing makes you so hot."

"Don't be like that."

There we stood sipping coke through straws, wallflowers in first bloom. Anne nudged me – she saw him first. Bill Taylor was edging his way round the rim of the dance floor. He appeared to be searching for someone – but not for us, for he looked right over our heads.

Then he must have suddenly realised he was looking through someone he knew:

"Hello."

"Hello," I gulped.

"I've just arrived. I was looking for the others," he said vaguely, still peering into the half light.

He must have realized it was a hopeless task. He shrugged his shoulders.

"Ah well – how's it going?"

"Fine," I lied.

A pause. "Would you like a dance?"

I couldn't believe it! But what about Anne? I gave her a questioning look.

"Will you be OK?"

"Go on!" She gave me a shove.

"Oh – hang on," I called to Bill. "My coke!" I explained.

I sucked vigorously and gulped the bubbles down – pushed the tin into Anne's hand and turned after him.

It was a jerky number, loud and tuneless and we'd just got into a kind of rhythmic waggle when the music stopped and we stood awkwardly facing each other, waiting for the music to start again.

It was a slow smooch, I realized, with a mixture of delight and horror. He looked at me for a split second and then, resigning himself to his fate, he put his arm lightly round my waist, his green cord jacket brushed against my cheek and I was in seventh heaven, his hand damp on my waist, the smell of the smoke on his breath, the music romantic, coiling its sound round us.

Then it happened, rather suddenly, and there was nothing I could do. I felt the bubbles of coke rising inside me. If I opened my mouth an enormous burp would emerge so I kept my mouth shut and tried to divert the air through my nose. There was an extraordinary sensation at the back of my throat and then a fine cascade of silver froth burst from my nostrils and tumbled down the front of Bill's green cord jacket.

"What's the matter!" he sprang away. I think he thought I was being sick.

"I'm so sorry – it was the coke – it came down my nose." I wiped ineffectually at his coat with my hand. Fortunately he laughed – and so did I and he wiped the lapel with a handkerchief but the music had finished and the spell had been broken. He saw his friends over the other side of the room and with a polite "Thanks – excuse me – I've just seen the others," he was gone.

I don't think I saw him again for weeks after that episode. It was my friend and dancing partner Anne who brought about the next development.

"My parents have said I can have a party on my birthday. Three weeks time, since it falls on a Saturday this year."

"Oh great! you can ask Bill!"

"Hang on! Hang on! First things first! Anyway how can we ask him? We don't know where he lives."

There were lots of preparations to fill the days; ordering drink, borrowing glasses from the pub, and the invitations to pass around. But the problem of how to invite Bill obsessed me. Finally Anne's brother Ed was enlisted to help. He knew Lawrence, who was Bill's best mate, and he'd tell them both. We couldn't be sure he'd come – but on the morning of the party Eddie swore for the tenth time that the message had been delivered.

The afternoon was taken up with the terrible labour of moving furniture, rolling carpets, putting vases and photos and breakables away, sprinkling ashtrays in the shape of saucers and shells, liberally around the front and back rooms. Eddie was in charge of records – music would be in the back room and we'd leave the heavy furniture in the front room for those who wanted to sit around and talk. Together we pushed the deep old-fashioned armchairs and settees back to the corners of the room and sprinkled the cushions over the rest of the floor.

I barely had time to bath and pull the blue check dress on again, wishing I had something else I could wear instead but there was no time to dwell on it. The blue stockings were sneaked out of my sister's drawer again and this time I picked up a blue pearly Alice band from her dressing table and brushed my hair loose and back behind my ears, pinning it neatly with this band.

By the time I arrived Anne was already in despair, crying her eyes out in her bedroom whilst a few guests clung to the walls and ate crisps downstairs.

"What's the matter? Anne? For goodness sake! Speak to me."

"It's a failure – nobody's going to come! I hate parties anyway."

"Don't be silly – there are lots of people here already. Things are always slow at the beginning, now come on!"

I wetted a flannel under the tap and patted her swollen eyes. I slipped her into her dress and brushed her hair for her till it shone.

"I look awful," she wailed.

"Nonsense – anyway there aren't many lights on and no-one will see."

Down we went together, I secretly feeling no more confident than she. But people were indeed arriving and Ed had an LP of Elvis Presley shaking the room. The kitchen was soon awash in beer and cider and the hallway blocked with people struggling to and fro holding paper cups aloft.

Anne and I stood at the bottom of the stairs by the telephone.

"Do you know all these people?" I asked her.

"No," she looked glum.

Then her face brightened suddenly as a gangly youth in a red crash helmet strode through the door.

"He's come!" she cried

"Who? Bill?"

"No – silly!"

And she darted off and up to him, taking his helmet to safety, the gracious hostess and birthday girl.

I recognized a couple of Anne's school mates and chatted to them before they slid away into the kitchen. I was about to follow when the door swung open again and this time it was Bill. My heart beat heavily and I felt myself colour. He looked round vacantly and then saw me.

"Hello again."

"Hello."

"I've come to the right place then."

"Yes."

"Where shall I put this?" He held a party beer can up.

"Follow the mass!"

"Right!"

And off he went leaving me to think of all the witty, arresting things I could have said:

24

"I'll take it through! Ah good, drink's arrived – I've been waiting for something good to walk through that door. Let's open it here."

I couldn't follow him now – it would be too obvious. I'd have to walk into the front room and pretend I was going there anyway. There were couples spread-eagled on the cushions, on the floor – wound together on the settee. Only the big armchair was unoccupied – I turned back and wandered into the dancing room. Eddie was standing by the record player watching the couples dancing where the dining room table usually stood.

"Having a good time?" he asked as I looked through the pile of records.

"Yes – in a way."

"Has he come then?"

"Who?" I flushed.

"Your Rover Scout."

"I don't know." I moved off again, into the kitchen for a glass of something. Empty bottles covered the sideboard and the kitchen table and I picked up each in turn.

"Here's some cider – do you like cider?" asked a strange man with little round glasses and a pale blue tee-shirt.

"If there's nothing else – thanks!"

He laughed – "Yes – I'm like that too. Stick to beer as long as it lasts and then as a last resort onto the cider – dry first – last of all, the sweet! Mind you – I'd go for the wine too, if it was around – wouldn't say no to a drop of the white. I prefer white to red myself. Got terribly drunk on the red once – mind you" – I shifted from one foot to the other trying to maintain interest – "not as bad as sherry – worst hangover ever I got from sherry. Can't touch it now. Even the smell – you know – sort of brings it all back." He laughed at his own wit. I smiled and moved as if to go.

"Do you want to dance?" he asked eagerly.

"Well – er – I'm a bit hot actually!"

"Oh." His face dropped for an instant.

"Well – it does make you sweat a bit, does dancing – anyway – you can't really talk – all this loud music – can't stand this one – whatever it is."

"It's Elvis!" I said hotly.

"Oh – you like it do you – no accounting for taste."

There was a pause and I seized my opportunity.

"Excuse me – I've got to go and join the queue!"

25

"Queue?" he looked blank.

"Bathroom."

"Oh I see – yes sure – I'll wait here."

Wait, would he! He'd have to wait a long time. I slipped out and back to my spot by the telephone.

"Come on," said a voice and I was gripped by the hand at the same time. I whirled round – it was Bill.

He led me to the front room, to the big armchair. He sat down and patted his knee, and I sat woodenly, like a ventriloquist's dummy. I don't think we said anything.

He settled back and I rested my head on that green cord jacket. I hardly dared breathe lest I should break the spell.

His hand was rubbing up and down my back gently. I almost fell asleep it was so soothing.

Then I felt him shifting and I lifted my head an inch or two – he was staring at me. I thought I should say something and was just about to when his lips closed on mine in my first kiss. He pushed hard and I could feel his teeth break the skin.

My pulse was beating. He was pulling my head down – suddenly I felt something had hit my nose – my pearly Alice band. My eyelashes caught against it – perhaps Bill's did too for he broke away and I was left panting with a blue Alice band across my eyes. He pulled it off and dropped it behind him onto the floor and with barely enough time to draw breath he pulled my mouth towards his – his lips forced mine open and our teeth chipped painfully.

So we kissed the night away, pausing only to surface for air and to pull wisps of my hair from our mouths whilst Elvis and Adam and Mick strummed their guitars.

Then it was all over. We were struggling up and lights were turned on. I stood blinking like an owl in the middle of the room while Bill lit a cigarette. Anne came scurrying in emptying ashtrays, collecting glasses and bottles.

"I'd better help," I said to Bill.

"Yes – sure – I must go – so long."

And that was that.

All that night I kept waking, gasping for breath, with his lips on mine and my heart thumping and next day I woke with a headache and a bruised chin. I saw him that very day coming towards me along the road. It was me who turned, cheeks hot, pulse beating and I walked quickly, obviously away from him.

I still don't know why.

Aspen Joycechild Womun

I am being born a woman human being

I am being born a woman human being
I have breasts and a soft body
I am made of soil and water and I look like a tree
I have quite a few scars, but I am growing more beautiful
  everyday not more perfect, just more me.
I have lost quite a bit of blood at the hands of jagged men
  cultivating me for commercial interest
I have removed myself from their cultivated plots
          where every tree must strive to look the same
          and be quiet and obedient
          and bear fruit (of the right kind) at their bidding
I have picked up my roots and wriggled my toes and stepped
  out gingerly into the world
I have not always had enough moisture to blossom forth
I may move again
Outside the forestry commission we roam the hills
and sniff life.

Pat Van Twest

when you accuse me of not being

when you accuse me of not being
like a woman
i wonder what like is
& how one becomes it.

i think woman is what
women are
& as i am one
so must that be included
in what woman is

So, therefore, i am like.

Julie Sapsford (age 14)

While Walking on a Wire Tightrope

Often, when I am walking on a wire tightrope.
It becomes so taut that it cuts my feet.
Occasionally, the wire splits me in two,
            and I fall,
One half to the left, the other to the right.
Normally, I fall trying to do tricks on a wire tightrope.

Sometimes, if I do not concentrate, I fall,
Sometimes, to the crowds, and am engulfed,
Sometimes, to the gaudy ringmaster in the
Sawdust circle.

Normally, I fall trying to do tricks on a wire tightrope.
Occasionally, the wire splits me in two,
            and I fall,
One half to the left, the other to the right.
Often when I am walking on a wire tightrope
It becomes so taut that it cuts my feet.

Elizabeth Bowen

Daffodils

Miss Murcheson stopped at the corner of the High Street to buy a bunch of daffodils from the flower-man. She counted out her money very carefully pouring a little stream of coppers from her purse into the palm of her hand.

" – ninepence – ten – eleven – pence halfpenny – a *shilling*! Thank you very much. Good afternoon."

A gust of wind rushed up the street, whirling her skirts up round her like a ballet-dancer's, and rustling the Reckitts-blue paper round the daffodils. The slender gold trumpets tapped and quivered against her face as she held them up with one hand and pressed her skirts down hastily with the other. She felt as though she had been enticed into a harlequinade by a company of Columbines who were quivering with laughter at her discomfiture; and looked round to see if anyone had witnessed her display of chequered moirette petticoat and the inches of black stocking above her boots. But the world remained unembarrassed.

Today the houses seemed taller and farther apart; the street wider and full of a bright, clear light that cast no shadows and was never sunshine. Under archways and between the houses the distances had a curious transparency, as though they had been painted upon glass. Against the luminous and indeterminate sky the Abbey tower rose distinct and delicate.

Miss Murcheson, forgetting all confusion, was conscious of her wings. She paused again to hitch up the bundle of exercise books slithering down beneath her elbow, then took the dipping road as a bird swings down into the air. Her mouth was faintly acrid with spring dust and the scent of daffodils was in her nostrils. As she left the High Street farther behind her, the traffic sounded as a faint and murmurous hum, striking here and there a tinkling note like wind-bells.

Under her detachment she was conscious of the houses, the houses and the houses. They were square, flat-faced and plaster-fronted, painted creams and greys and buffs; one, a purplish-rose colour. Venetian shutters flat against the wall broadened the line of the windows, there were coloured fanlights over all the doors. Spiked railings before them shut off their little squares of grass or gravel from the road and between the railings branches swung out to brush against her dress and recall her to the wonder of their budding loveliness.

Miss Murcheson remembered that her mother would be out for tea, and quickened her steps in anticipation of that delightful solitude. The silver birch tree that distinguished their front garden slanted beckoning her across the pavement. She hesitated, as her gate swung open, and stood looking up and down the road. She was sorry to go in, but could not resist the invitation of the empty house. She wondered if tomorrow would fill her with so strange a stirring as today. Soon, in a few months, it would be summer and there would be nothing more to come. Summer would be beautiful, but this spring made promise of a greater beauty than summer could fulfil; hinted at a mystery which other summers had evaded rather than explained. She went slowly up the steps, fumbling for her latch-key.

The day's dinner still hung dank and heavy in the air of the little hall. She stood in the doorway, with that square of light and sound behind her, craving the protection and the comfort with which that dark entrance had so often received her. There was a sudden desolation in the emptiness of the house.

Quickly she entered the sitting-room and flung open the window, which set the muslin curtains swaying in the breeze and clanked the little pictures on the walls. The window embrasure was so deep that there was little light in the corners of the room; armchairs and cabinets were lurking in the dusk. The square of daylight by the window was blocked by a bamboo table groaning under an array of photographs. In her sweeping mood she deposed the photographs, thrust the table to one side, and pulled her chair up into the window. "I can't correct my essays in the dark," she asserted, though she had done so every evening of the year.

"How tight-laced you are, poor Columbines," she said, throwing away the paper and seeing how the bass cut deep into the fleshy stems. "You were brave above it all, but – there now!" She cut the bass and shook the flowers out into a vase. "I can't correct," she sighed, "with you all watching me. You are so terribly flippant!"

31

But what a curious coincidence: she had set her class to write an essay upon Daffodils! "You shall judge; I'll read them all out loud. They *will* amuse you." She dipped her pen in the red-ink pot with an anticipatory titter.

With a creak of wheels a young woman went by slowly, wheeling a perambulator. She leant heavily on the handle-bar, tilting the perambulator on its two back wheels, and staring up, wide-mouthed, at the windows.

"How nice to be so much interested," thought Miss Murcheson, pressing open the first exercise-book. "But I'm sure it can't be a good thing for the baby."

The essays lacked originality. Each paragraph sidled up self-consciously to openings for a suitable quotation, to rush each one through with a gasp of triumph.

> And then my heart with pleasure fills
> And dances with the daffodils.

> Fair daffodils, we weep to see
> You fade away so soon

She wondered if any of her class could weep for the departure of a daffodil. Mostly they had disclaimed responsibility for such weakness by the stern prefix, "As the poet says –". Flora Hopwood had, she remembered, introduced a "Quotation Dictionary", which must have been round her circle.

"I must forbid it. Why can't they see things for themselves, think them out? I don't believe they ever really see anything, just accept things on the authority of other people. I could make them believe anything. What a responsibility teaching is – But is it? They'd believe me, but they wouldn't care. It wouldn't matter, really.

"They're so horribly used to things. Nothing ever comes new to them that they haven't grown up with. They get their very feelings out of books. Nothing ever surprises or impresses them. When spring comes they get preoccupied, stare dreamily out of the windows. They're thinking out their new hats. Oh, if only I didn't know them quite so well, or knew them a little better!

"If I had a school of my own," she meditated, running her eyes down the pages and mechanically underlining spelling-mistakes, "I would make them think. I'd horrify them, if nothing better. But here – how ever can one, teaching at a High School? Miss Peterson would –

"They *do* like me. At least, one set does, I know. I'm rather a cult, they appreciate my Titian hair. They'd like me more, though, if I knew how to do it better, and knew better how to use my eyes. Their sentimentality embarrasses me. In a way they're so horribly mature, I feel at a disadvantage with them. If only they'd be a little more spontaneous. But spontaneity is beyond them at present. They're simply calves, after all, rather sophisticated calves."

She dreamed, and was awakened by familiar laughter. Nobody's laughter in particular, but surely it was the laughter of the High School? Three girls were passing with arms close linked, along the pavement underneath her window. She looked down on the expressive, tilted ovals of their sailor hats; then, on an impulse, smacked the window-sill to attract their attention. Instantly they turned up three pink faces of surprise, which broadened into smiles of recognition.

"Hullo, Miss Murcheson!"

"Hullo, children! Come in for a minute and talk to me. I'm all alone."

Millicent, Rosemary and Doris hesitated, eyeing one another, poised for flight. "Righto!" they agreed unanimously.

Miss Murcheson, all of a flutter, went round to open the front door. She looked back at the sitting-room as though she had never seen it before.

Why had she asked them in, those terrible girls whom she had scarcely spoken to? They would laugh at her, they would tell the others.

The room was full of them, of their curiosity and embarrassment and furtive laughter. She had never realized what large girls they were; how plump and well-developed. She felt them eyeing her stack of outraged relatives, the photographs she swept off on to a chair; their eyes flitted from the photographs to the daffodils, from the daffodils to the open, red-scored exercise books.

"Yes," she said, "your writings, I daresay. Do you recognize them? I was correcting 'Daffodils' and they made me dreary – sit down, won't you? – *dreary*. I wonder if any of you have ever used your senses; smelt, or *seen* things – Oh, *do* sit down!"

She seemed to be shouting into a forest of thick bodies. They seated themselves along the edge of an ottoman in a bewildered row; this travestied their position in the class-room and made her feel, facing them, terribly official and instructive. She tried to shake this off.

"It's cruel, isn't it, to lie in wait for you like this and pull you in and lecture you about what you don't feel about daffodils!"

Her nervous laughter tinkled out into silence.

"It was a beastly subject," said someone, heavily.

"Beastly? Oh, Mill – Rosemary, have you never seen a daffodil?"

They giggled.

"No, but looked at one?" Her earnestness swept aside her embarrassment. "Not just heard about them – 'Oh yes, daffodils: yellow flowers; spring, mother's vases, bulbs, borders, flashing past flower-shop windows' – but taken one up in your hands and felt it?"

How she was haranguing them!

"It's very difficult to be clever about things one's *used* to," said Millicent. "That's why history essays are so much easier. You tell us about things, and we just write them down."

"That's why you're so lazy; you're using *my* brains; just giving me back what I gave you again, a little bit the worse for the wear."

They looked hurt and uncomfortable.

Doris got up and walked over to the fireplace.

("Good," thought Miss Murcheson, "it will relieve the tension a bit if they will only begin to prowl.")

"What a pretty photograph, Miss Murcheson. Who is it? Not – not *you*?"

"*Me*?" said Miss Murcheson with amusement. "Yes. Why not? Does it surprise you, then?"

"You've got such a *dinky* hat on!" cried the girl, with naive astonishment.

The others crowded round her.

"You look so different," said Doris, still scrutinizing the photograph. "Awfully happy, and prosperous, and – cocksure."

"Perhaps it was the hat!" suggested Millicent.

"Oh, *Millicent*! No, I'm sure Miss Murcheson was *thinking* about something else."

"Or somebody."

"Oh, Doris, you are awful!"

They all giggled, and glanced apprehensively across at her. She wondered why she was not more offended by them.

"As a matter of fact," she enlightened them, "*that* was

because of daffodils. It just illustrates my point, curiously enough."

They were still absorbed.

"Oh, Miss *Murcheson*!"

"*Miss* Murcheson!"

"When was it taken?"

"Last Easter holidays. Nearly a year ago. At Seabrooke. By a friend of mine."

"*Do-oo* give me one!"

" – And me?"

"I'm afraid that's the only print I've got; and that's mother's."

"Were there more?"

"Yes, various people took them. You see, I haven't faced a real camera for years, so when I got these snaps they were scrambled for by people who'd been asking me for photos."

"People?" She was rising visibly in their estimation.

"Oh yes. Friends."

"Why *daffodils*?" reverted Rosemary.

"Somebody had just given me a great big bunch." She was impressed by their interest. "I wonder if daffodils will ever make any of you look like that."

"It all depends, you see," said Millicent, astutely. "Nobody has ever given us any. If they *did* perhaps –"

"*Really*?" said Miss Murcheson, with innocent concern. "Take all those, if they would really inspire you! No, dears, I'd *like* you to."

She gathered the daffodils together and lifted them, dripping, from the vase.

The girls retreated.

"Oh no, really, *not* your daffodils –"

"We don't mean –"

"Not *your* daffodils, Miss Murcheson. It wasn't *that* a bit."

Evidently a false move on her part. She was bewildered by them; could not fathom the depths of their cinema-bred romanticism.

Doris had put away the photograph and stood with her back to the others, fingering the ornaments on the chimney-piece.

"There are lots of things," she said rapidly, "that you only feel because of people. That's the only reason things are there for, I *think*. You wouldn't notice them otherwise, or care about them. It's only sort of –" she stopped. Her ears glowed crimson underneath her hat.

"Association," they sighed, ponderously.

"That's exactly what's the matter," cried Miss Murcheson. "We've got all the nice, fresh, independent, outside things so smeared over with our sentimentalities and prejudices and – associations – that we can't see them anyhow but as part of ourselves. That's how you're – we're missing things and spoiling things for ourselves. You – we don't seem able to *discover*."

"Life," said Doris sententiously, "is a very big adventure. Of course we all see *that*."

The other two looked at her quickly. All three became suddenly hostile. She was encouraging them to outrage the decencies of conversation. It was bad form, this flagrant discussion of subjects only for their most secret and fervid whisperings.

To her, they were still unaccountable. She had not wished to probe.

"I don't think that's what I meant," she said a little flatly. "Of course your lives will be full of interesting things, and those will be your own affairs. Only, if I could be able, I'm always trying, to make you care about the little fine things you might pass over, that have such big roots underground."

"I should like you to be happy as I've been, as I'm going to be," she said impulsively. "I should love to watch you after you've left my form, going up and up the school, and getting bigger, and then, when you've left, going straight and clearly to the essential things."

The tassel of the blind cord tapped against the window-sill, through the rustling curtains they looked out on to the road.

They had awaited a disclosure intimate and personal. The donor of those last year's daffodils had taken form, portentous in their minds. But she had told them nothing, given them the stone of her abstract, colourless idealism while they sat there, open-mouthed for sentimental bread.

"Won't you stay to tea?" she asked. "Oh, *do*. We'll picnic; boil the kettle on the gas-ring, and eat sticky buns – I've got a bag of sticky buns. We'll have a party in honour of the daffodils."

The prospect allured her, it would be a fantastic interlude.

They all got up.

"Doris and Millicent are coming to tea with me, Miss

Murcheson. Mother's expecting us, thanks most awfully. Else we should have loved to."

"We should have loved to," echoed the others. "Thanks most awfully."

She felt a poignant disappointment and relief, as standing with her eyes on the daffodils, she heard the children clattering down the steps.

Tomorrow they will be again impersonal; three pink moons in a firmament of faces.

The three, released, eyed one another with a common understanding.

"Miss Murcheson has never really *lived*," said Doris.

They linked arms again and sauntered down the road.

Dorothy Parker

A Telephone Call

Please, God, let him telephone me now. Dear God, let him call me now. I won't ask anything else of You, truly I won't. It isn't very much to ask. It would be so little to You. God, such a little, little thing. Only let him telephone now. Please, God. Please, please, please.

If I didn't think about it, maybe the telephone might ring. Sometimes it does that. If I could think of something else. If I could think of something else. Maybe if I counted five hundred by fives, it might ring by that time. I'll count slowly. I won't cheat. And if it rings when I get to three hundred, I won't stop; I won't answer it until I get to five hundred. Five, ten, fifteen, twenty, twenty-five, thirty, thirty-five, forty, forty-five, fifty. . . . Oh, please ring. Please.

This is the last time I'll look at the clock. I will not look at it again. It's ten minutes past seven. He said he would telephone at five o'clock. "I'll call you at five, darling." I think that's where he said "darling." I'm almost sure he said it there. I know he called me "darling" twice, and the other time was when he said good-by. "Good-by, darling." He was busy, and he can't say much in the office, but he called me "darling" twice. He couldn't have minded my calling him up. I know you shouldn't keep telephoning them – I know they don't like that. When you do that, they know you are thinking about them and wanting them, and that makes them hate you. But I hadn't talked to him in three days – not in three days. And all I did was ask him how he was; it was just the way anybody might have called him up. He couldn't have minded that. He couldn't have thought I was bothering him. "No, of course you're not," he said. And he said he'd telephone me. He didn't have to say that. I didn't ask him to, truly I didn't. I'm sure I didn't. I don't think he would say he'd telephone me, and then just never do it. Please don't let him do that, God. Please don't.

"I'll call you at five, darling." "Good-by, darling." He was busy, and he was in a hurry, and there were people around him, but he called me "darling" twice. That's mine, that's mine. I have that, even if I never see him again. Oh, but that's so little. That isn't enough. Nothing's enough, if I never see him again. Please let me see him again, God. Please, I want him so much. I want him so much. I'll be good, God. I will try to be better, I will, if You will let me see him again. If you let him telephone me. Oh, let him telephone me now.

Ah, don't let my prayer seem too little to You, God. You sit up there, so white and old, with all the angels about You and the stars slipping by. And I come to You with a prayer about a telephone call. Ah, don't laugh, God. You see, You don't know how it feels. You're so safe, there on Your throne, with the blue swirling under You. Nothing can touch You; no one can twist Your heart in his hands. This is suffering, God, this is bad, bad suffering. Won't You help me? For Your Son's sake, help me. You said You would do whatever was asked of You in His name. Oh, God, in the name of Thine only beloved Son, Jesus Christ, our Lord, let him telephone me now.

I must stop this. I mustn't be this way. Look. Suppose a young man says he'll call a girl up, and then something happens, and he doesn't. That isn't so terrible, is it? Why, it's going on all over the world, right this minute. Oh, what do I care what's going on all over the world? Why can't that telephone ring? Why can't it, why can't it? Couldn't you ring? Ah, please, couldn't you? You damned, ugly, shiny thing. It would hurt you to ring, wouldn't it? Oh, that would hurt you. Damn you, I'll pull your filthy roots out of the wall, I'll smash your smug black face in little bits. Damn you to hell.

No, no, no. I must stop. I must think about something else. This is what I'll do. I'll put the clock in the other room. Then I can't look at it. If I do have to look at it, then I'll have to walk into the bedroom, and that will be something to do. Maybe, before I look at it again, he will call me. I'll be so sweet to him, if he calls me. If he says he can't see me tonight, I'll say, "Why, that's all right, dear. Why, of course it's all right." I'll be the way I was when I first met him. Then maybe he'll like me again. I was always sweet, at first. Oh, it's so easy to be sweet to people before you love them.

I think he must still like me a little. He couldn't have called me "darling" twice today, if he didn't still like me a little. It isn't all gone, if he still likes me a little; even if it's only a little,

little bit. You see, God, if You would just let him telephone me I wouldn't have to ask You anything more. I would be sweet to him. I would be gay, I would be just the way I used to be, and then he would love me again. And then I would never have to ask You for anything more. Don't You see, God? So won't You please let him telephone me? Won't You please, please, please?

Are You punishing me, God, because I've been bad? Are you angry with me because I did that? Oh, but, God, there are so many bad people – You could not be hard only to me. And it wasn't very bad; it couldn't have been bad. We didn't hurt anybody, God. Things are only bad when they hurt people. We didn't hurt one single soul; You know that. You know it wasn't bad, don't You, God? So won't You let him telephone me now? If he doesn't telephone me, I'll know God is angry with me. I'll count five hundred by fives, and if he hasn't called me then, I will know God isn't going to help me, ever again. That will be the sign. Five, ten, fifteen, twenty, twenty-five, thirty, thirty-five, forty, forty-five, fifty, fifty-five. . . . It was bad. I knew it was bad. All right, God, send me to hell. You think You're frightening me with Your hell, don't You? You think Your hell is worse than mine.

I mustn't. I mustn't do this. Suppose he's a little late calling me up – that's nothing to get hysterical about. Maybe he isn't going to call – maybe he's coming straight up here without telephoning. He'll be cross if he sees I have been crying. They don't like you to cry. He doesn't cry. I wish to God I could make him cry. I wish I could make him cry and tread the floor and feel his heart heavy and big and festering in him. I wish I could hurt him like hell.

He doesn't wish that about me. I don't think he even knows how he makes me feel. I wish he could know, without my telling him. They don't like you to tell them they've made you cry. They don't like you to tell them you're unhappy because of them. If you do, they think you're possessive and exacting. And then they hate you. They hate you whenever you say anything you really think. You always have to keep playing little games. Oh, I thought we didn't have to; I thought this was so big I could say whatever I meant. I guess you can't, ever. I guess there isn't ever anything big enough for that. Oh, if he would just telephone, I wouldn't tell him I had been sad about him. They hate sad people. I would be so sweet and so gay, he couldn't help but like me. If he would only telephone. If he would only telephone.

Maybe that's what he is doing. Maybe he is coming on here without calling me up. Maybe he's on his way now. Something might have happened to him. No, nothing could ever happen to him. I can't picture anything happening to him. I never picture him run over. I never see him lying still and long and dead. I wish he were dead. That's a terrible wish. That's a lovely wish. If he were dead, he would be mine. If he were dead, I would never think of now and the last few weeks. I would remember only the lovely times. It would be all beautiful. I wish he were dead. I wish he were dead, dead, dead.

This is silly. It's silly to go wishing people were dead just because they don't call you up the very minute they said they would. Maybe the clock's fast; I don't know whether it's right. Maybe he's hardly late at all. Anything could have made him a little late. Maybe he had to stay at his office. Maybe he went home, to call me up from there, and somebody came in. He doesn't like to telephone me in front of people. Maybe he's worried, just a little, little bit, about keeping me waiting. He might even hope that I would call him up. I could do that. I could telephone him.

I mustn't. I mustn't, I mustn't. Oh, God, please don't let me telephone him. Please keep me from doing that. I know, God, just as well as You do, that if he were worried about me, he'd telephone no matter where he was or how many people there were around him. Please make me know that, God. I don't ask You to make it easy for me – You can't do that, for all that You could make a world. Only let me know it, God. Don't let me go on hoping. Don't let me say comforting things to myself. Please don't let me hope, dear God. Please don't.

I won't telephone him. I'll never telephone him again as long as I live. He'll rot in hell, before I'll call him up. You don't have to give me strength. God; I have it myself. If he wanted me, he could get me. He knows where I am. He knows I'm waiting here. He's so sure of me, so sure. I wonder why they hate you, as soon as they are sure of you. I should think it would be so sweet to be sure.

It would be so easy to telephone him. Then I'd know. Maybe it wouldn't be a foolish thing to do. Maybe he wouldn't mind. Maybe he'd like it. Maybe he has been trying to get me. Sometimes people try and try to get you on the telephone, and they say the number doesn't answer. I'm not just saying that to help myself; that really happens. You know that really happens. God. Oh, God, keep me away from that telephone. Keep me away. Let me still have just a little bit of pride. I think I'm going to need it. God. I think it will be all I'll have.

Oh, what does pride matter, when I can't stand it if I don't talk to him? Pride like that is such a silly, shabby little thing. The real pride, the big pride, is in having no pride. I'm not saying that just because I want to call him. I am not. That's true, I know that's true. I will be big. I will be beyond little prides.

Please, God, keep me from telephoning him. Please, God.

I don't see what pride has to do with it. This is such a little thing, for me to be bringing in pride, for me to be making such a fuss about. I may have misunderstood him. Maybe he said for me to call him up, at five. "Call me at five, darling." He could have said that, perfectly well. It's so possible that I didn't hear him right. "Call me at five, darling." I'm almost sure that's what he said. God, don't let me talk this way to myself. Make me know, please make me know.

I'll think about something else. I'll just sit quietly. If I could sit still. If I could sit still. Maybe I could read. Oh, all the books are about people who love each other, truly and sweetly. What do they want to write about that for? Don't they know it isn't true? Don't they know it's a lie, it's a God damned lie? What do they have to tell about that for, when they know how it hurts? Damn them, damn them, damn them.

I won't. I'll be quiet. This is nothing to get excited about. Look. Suppose he were someone I didn't know very well. Suppose he were another girl. Then I'd just telephone and say, "Well, for goodness' sake, what happened to you?" That's what I'd do, and I'd never even think about it. Why can't I be casual and natural, just because I love him? I can be. Honestly, I can be. I'll call him up, and be so easy and pleasant. You see if I won't, God. Oh, don't let me call him. Don't, don't, don't.

God, aren't You really going to let him call me? Are you sure, God? Couldn't You please relent? Couldn't You? I don't even ask You to let him telephone me this minute, God: only let him do it in a little while. I'll count five hundred by fives. I'll do it so slowly and so fairly. If he hasn't telephoned then, I'll call him. I will. Oh, please, dear God, dear kind God, my blessed Father in Heaven, let him call before then. Please, God. Please.

Five, ten, fifteen, twenty, twenty-five, thirty, thirty-five. . . .

Ntozake Shange

Lady in Red

without any assistance or guidance from you
i have loved you assiduously for 8 months 2 wks & a day
i have been stood up four times
i've left 7 packages on yr doorstep
forty poems 2 plants & 3 handmade notecards i left
town so i cd send to you have been no help to me
on my job
you call at 3:00 in the mornin on weekdays
so i cd drive 27½ miles cross the bay before i go to work
charmin charmin
but you are of no assistance
i want you to know
this waz an experiment
to see how selfish i cd be
if i wd really carry on to snare a possible lover
if i waz capable of debasin my self for the love of another
if i cd stand not being wanted
when i wanted to be wanted
& i cannot
so
with no further assistance & no guidance from you
i am endin this affair

this note is attached to a plant
i've been waterin since the day i met you
you may water it
yr damn self

Queen Elizabeth I

When I was Fair and Young

When I was fair and young and favour gracèd me,
Of many was I sought, their mistress for to be:
But I did scorn them all, and answered them therefore,
 "Go, go, go, seek some other where:
  Importune me no more."

How many weeping eyes I made to pine with woe,
How many sighing hearts, I have no skill to show:
Yet I the prouder grew, and answered them therefore,
 "Go, go, go, seek some other where:
  Importune me no more."

Then spake fair Venus' son, that proud victorious boy,
And said, "Fine Dame, since that you be so coy,
I will so pluck your plumes that you shall say no more,
 'Go, go, go, seek some other where:
  Importune me no more.' "

When he had spake these words, such change grew in my
  breast
That neither night nor day, since that, I could take any
  rest:
Than lo, I did repent that I had said before,
 "Go, go, go, seek some other where:
  Importune me no more."

Anna Akhmatova

I Wrung My Hands

I wrung my hands under my dark veil . . .
"Why are you pale, what makes you reckless?"
– Because I have made my loved one drunk
with an astringent sadness.

I'll never forget. He went out, reeling;
his mouth was twisted, desolate . . .
I ran downstairs, not touching the banisters,
and followed him as far as the gate.

And shouted, choking: "I meant it all
in fun. Don't leave me, or I'll die of pain."
He smiled at me – oh so calmly, terribly –
and said: "Why don't you get out of the rain?"

Translated from the Russian by
Max Hayward and Stanley Kunitz

Elizabeth Barrett Browning

How Do I Love Thee?

How do I love thee? Let me count the ways.
I love thee to the depth and breadth and height
My soul can reach, when feeling out of sight
For the ends of Being and ideal Grace.
I love thee to the level of every day's
Most quiet need, by sun and candlelight.
I love thee freely, as men strive for Right;
I love thee purely, as they turn from Praise.
I love thee with the passion put to use
In my old griefs, and with my childhood's faith.
I love thee with a love I seemed to lose
With my lost saints, – I love thee with the breath,
Smiles, tears, of all my life! – and, if God choose,
I shall but love thee better after death.

Glenda Adams

Reclamation

This is the story of a body, my body, and of the many efforts that have been made to separate us.

THE THROAT

The throat is white. Blue-white. Grey-white. Across the throat is a white scar, once pink, and before that red. When the head is thrown back, in pain or terror, the throat is stretched tight and the scream can be seen as it forms.

Men are drawn to this scar. Some wait for weeks or months before asking why. Others ask immediately. I try to please them and give each the story he wishes to hear. To one, who asked immediately, shouting above the other shouting party voices, I said: Once, when I was freckled and hopeful I fell in love. He was a French-horn player in the band of the Royal Irish Guards. He wore a red coat and black trousers and played Andalusia, Dance of the Clowns, and *Besame Mucho*. But he left my life. I failed to kill myself for I did not know where to cut.

This story pleased the party man and increased his fascination. He took me aside, away from the shouting voices, and talked to me softly about himself, his face close to mine. He told me how sad his life had been, how his misfortunes had been far greater than mine, how he was searching for love, for a woman who would understand and care for him. He held my hand. Then he stroked my forearm and traced patterns on the inside of my elbow. He squeezed my shoulder and outlined my ear and my jaw with his fingers. And finally holding his breath, he touched my throat and the scar, with his two thumbs. "Would you do the same for me?" he asked.

Another man, one who seemed to offer a refuge, advised me to wear pullovers with high turtlenecks and long sleeves in order to hide my body and my story.

Here is the real story of the scar: When I was an infant, so they tell me, my father poured a freshly brewed pot of tea on me. An accident. They removed my hot, wet clothes and explored my body to see what damage had been done. It was then, among the folds of skin under the chin, that they discovered the birthmark, small and round, the size of a penny and the color of tea with cream.

The birthmark grew with me to the size of a silver dollar. My treasure island, beneath which lay buried my voice.

"We'll have to do something about it. Remove it. It looks terrible," my mother said one year as she looked at our vacation pictures. "They can cut things out these days and it hardly leaves a mark." She held a photograph in which I stood on a narrow rock path that wound down the face of a cliff to the breaking ocean waves. My father had taken the photograph from the top of the cliff. He had called out instructions as I climbed unwillingly down the path toward the sea. I was frightened and told him I did not want to go any further, but he told me not to be silly and described to me how spectacular the photograph would be. From where I stood, between my father and the ocean, I could scarcely hear his voice. I wore wildflowers in my belt, banksia and sarsaparilla, and before he took the photograph my father called to me to hold the flowers in my hands, in front of me at my waist. He told me to turn my back to the sea and look up toward him. He told me to lift my chin and look right up at him and smile. "I can't," I said, "It makes me dizzy." I stood close to the cliff face and closed my eyes. I rested my cheek against the sandstone of the cliff.

"Don't be a baby," he called. He said he was losing his patience. "Step back a little, then look up, and smile."

To please him, and to get it over with, I stepped back to the edge of the path and turned my face to him. But I could not smile, for I was too afraid.

"What a spectacular shot," my mother said as she held the photograph. "Wonderful churning waves. But that birthmark will have to go. You'll be grateful later on, when you're thinking about boys."

And the birthmark went. They bought me a nightgown and a blue chenille dressing gown to take to the hospital, the way they bought a new bedjacket for my grandmother before she died.

"They are going to cut your throat," my brother said.

The doctor bent over me with the needle. "You'll forget it

ever existed," he said. "No one will ever know. And by the time you're looking at boys, there won't even be a scar to spoil it."

"But I need my birthmark," I said.

THE VOICE

The voice became inaudible, even when it called for help or cried out in pain or made a simple request. When the voice said: "Please pass the teapot," there was silence until he, who ever he happened to be, said: "Mmmm? Did you say something?"

Another he, placing his ear before my mouth and frowning, said: "What did you say your name was?" before he drifted away.

The one who advised turtleneck sweaters said: "Stay with me and I'll take care of you."

THE HAIR, THE FACE, THE TEETH

The hair and the face were once the timid brown of the mouse.

At first the hair was long. It grew straight and was worn always in braids. I longed to let it fly free, to shake my head and feel my hair as I ran. But my mother said braids were for my own good, for no dirt or leaf or twig or louse could then find a home on me.

I brushed my hair every morning on the back verandah in the sun. My mother left me alone for fifteen minutes to brush and braid.

I brushed the hair counting the strokes, and when I had done I let my head fall back and felt the long brown hair against my back. I took the strands of hair from the brush and stood in the yard among the bushes and trees and held out my hand. The magpies came swooping and calling to fetch it for their nests. Sometimes the magpies raided my very head and plucked at the living strands.

When my brother watched the brushing, he said: "Your hair is the color of mud, and your face is a dirty mud puddle."

Once my father came onto the verandah and said: "Here, let me show you how to do it. None of those weak, halfhearted strokes." He took the brush and brushed so hard that he had to place his left hand about my neck, at the base of the throat, to brace himself for each stroke. There were red marks on my forehead and neck where he brought the brush down. Then he braided the hair, pulling it back so tight that the skin of my face felt it would split.

I cried out in pain and my mother came. "She's old enough to do that herself," she said.

"The hair should be cut off," said my father.

The next day as I stood brushing and thinking, my mother came with a towel and a pair of scissors and said it would save time in the mornings and be altogether less trouble if I had short hair.

"But I need my hair," I said.

She cut the hair short and ragged, so that it covered the forehead, the ears, the cheeks and the jawbone.

"Your head is a coconut that should be smashed open," said my brother.

"Stylish these days," said my mother, "and at least the forehead is covered, it is too broad and high, and the cheeks and jaw are covered, they are too prominent. Make the most of your good feature. Smile a lot. Without those teeth you would be nothing."

"I shall kick your teeth in," said my brother, and he often tried to.

My father said nothing. He stood and watched the cutting of the hair, his jaws clamped together.

Those brown tight braids now lie in a show box lined with tissue paper in the top drawer of my dresser.

THE HANDS AND WRISTS

The hands are older than their years. They are torn and scarred. The life line is difficult to trace. The fingertips are blunt, the nails are square. The fingers of the hands were once always folded under, out of sight, in the safety of the clenched fist.

The thumbs are double-jointed.

"All the better to string you up by," said my brother, who proved that two thumbs tied together with several strands of mere cotton thread render the body more helpless than thick ropes binding the arms and legs.

There is an indentation around the base of the ring finger, but it is the type of scar that will disappear in due course.

The wrists are smooth and white and unmarked, with veins that are a beautiful slate blue.

THE FEET

The feet faithfully followed the man who offered a refuge.

Once we picked our way through a vast and complex swamp. The aim was to get some exercise, some fresh air, to get away from people and spend a day close to nature, and to finish a roll of film. "Stay very close," said the man, "for it is easy to get completely lost in a swamp like this. You should have worn something bright. There are patches of water and ponds hidden in the reeds. Just follow me."

I stayed very close. I marked his footsteps, my eyes lowered watching his heels. We stopped to eat a peach and drink tea from the flask we had brought. We ate and drank standing up, for the ground was too wet for sitting.

"This mud is a nuisance," he said. "We must find higher, drier ground."

We walked, without speaking, for an hour or two, and after a while I found I did not have to concentrate so hard to follow. I was able to note the bushes and swamp flowers that thrived in the wet. There were small stones and masses of various browns and greens. I watched the water bubble from the earth beneath the weight of our feet. And soon, by narrowing my eyes, I perceived that we were walking on the surface of the water itself. The water was brown and it covered the brown earth in a fine film. I no longer was able to mark his footsteps. He was walking quickly, and the water covered his footprints. But I followed the slapping, splashing sound of his feet and the snapping of the reeds that broke as he passed.

I contemplated my feet standing in and on the muddy water. And as I looked I saw in the water the clouds, the sky, and a bird flying. I saw the reeds and the swamp flowers reflected and transforming the brown, flat opaque swamp water. I shifted my weight and the water rippled, and the reflections changed and rippled. Even with my head bowed and my eyes lowered in customary fear I saw the world. And then I straightened my back and raised my eyes to look about me.

I saw that I was alone. He had gone on and left me behind. I called, but he did not hear or he did not answer. I listened for the splashing of his feet, but I heard only the splashing and the cracking of the swamp creatures.

I thought: if I had kept my mind on what I was doing and followed him closely, I would be safe now.

But I laughed, and I kept looking about and refused to shed tears.

I found my own way home. But he was not there. And he did not come. And I waited, while my hair grew long, wanting to show him my new voice and my new face and my new straight back and my new unclenched hands. Until I knew that when I stopped following him in the swamp that day it was he who had gotten lost.

My feet are firm and straight and strong and white. They have walked at the edge of the sea. They have walked around the rim of the volcano and felt the heat of the rock. And they are at ease in the soft, damp browns of the swamp. And now I often feel free enough not to smile.

Mary Lavin

Sarah

Sarah had a bit of a bad name. That was the worst her neighbours would say of her, although there was a certain fortuity
about her choice of fathers for the three strapping sons she'd
borne – all three outside wedlock.

Sarah was a great worker, strong and tireless, and a lot of
women in the village got her in to scrub for them. Nobody was
ever known to be unkind to her. And not one of her children
was born in the County Home. It was the most upright matron
in the village who slapped life into every one of them.

"She's unfortunate, that's all," this matron used to say.
"How could she know any better – living with two rough
brothers? And don't forget she had no father herself!"

If Sarah had been one to lie in bed on a Sunday and miss
Mass, her neighbours might have felt differently about her,
there being greater understanding in their hearts for sins against
God than for sins against his Holy Church. But Sarah found it
easy to keep the Commandments of the church. She never
missed Mass. She observed abstinence on all days abstinence
was required. She frequently did the Stations of the Cross as
well. And on Lady Day when an annual pilgrimage took place
to a holy well in the neighbouring village Sarah was an example
to all – with her shoes off walking over the sharp flinty stones,
doing penance like a nun. If on that occasion some outsider
showed disapproval of her, Sarah's neighbours were quicker
than Sarah herself to take offence. All the same, charity was
tempered with prudence, and women with grown sons, and
women not long married, took care not to hire her.

So when Oliver Kedrigan's wife, a newcomer to the locality,
spoke of getting Sarah in to keep house for her while she was
going up to Dublin for a few days, two of the older women in
the district felt it their duty to step across to Kedrigan's and
offer a word of advice.

"I know she has a bit of a bad name," Kathleen conceded,

"but she's a great worker. I hear it's said she can bake bread that's nearly as good as my own."

"That may be!" said one of the women, "but if I was you, I'd think twice before I'd leave her to mind your house while you're away!"

"Who else is there I can get?" Kathleen said stubbornly.

"Why do you want anyone? You'll only be gone for three days, isn't that all?"

"Three days is a long time to leave a house in the care of a man."

"I'd rather let the roof fall in on him than draw Sarah Murray about my place!" said the woman. "She has a queer way of looking at a man. I wouldn't like to have her give my man one of those looks." Kathleen got their meaning at last.

"I can trust Oliver," she said coldly.

"It's not right to trust any man too far," the women said, shaking their heads.

"Oliver isn't that sort," Kathleen said, and her pale papery face smiled back contempt for the other women.

Stung by that smile, the women stood up and prepared to take their leave.

"I suppose you know your own business," said the first one who had raised the subject, "but I wouldn't trust the greatest saint ever walked with Sarah Murray."

"I'd trust Oliver with any woman in the world," Kathleen said.

"Well he's your man, not ours," said the two women, speaking together as they went out the door. Kathleen looked after them resentfully. She may not have been too happy herself about hiring Sarah but as she closed the door on the women she made up her mind for once and for all to do so, goaded on by pride in her legitimate power over her man. She'd let everyone see she could trust him.

As the two women went down the road they talked for a while about the Kedrigans but gradually they began to talk about other things, until they came to the lane leading up to the cottage where Sarah Murray lived with her brothers and the houseful of children. Looking up at the cottage their thoughts went back to the Kedrigans again and they came to a stand. "What ever took possession of Oliver Kedrigan to marry that bleached out bloodless thing?" one of them said.

"I don't know," said the other one. "But I wonder why she's going up to Dublin?"

"Why do you think!" said the first woman, contemptuous of her companion's ignorance. "Not that she looks to me like a woman would ever have a child, no matter how many doctors she might go to – in Dublin or elsewhere."

Sarah went over to Mrs Kedrigan's the morning Mrs Kedrigan was going away and she made her a nice cup of tea. Then she carried the suitcase down to the road and helped Kathleen on to the bus because it was a busy time for Oliver. He had forty lambing ewes and there was a predatory vixen in a nearby wood that was causing him alarm. He had had to go out at the break of day to put up a new fence.

But the bus was barely out of sight, when Oliver's cart rattled back into the yard. He'd forgotten to take the wire-cutters with him. He drew up outside the kitchen door and called to Sarah to hand him out the clippers, so he wouldn't have to get down off the cart. But when he looked down at her, he gave a laugh. "Did you rub sheep-raddle into your cheeks?" he asked, and he laughed again – a loud happy laugh that could give no offence. And Sarah took none. But her cheeks went redder, and she angrily swiped a bare arm across her face as if to stem the flux of the healthy blood in her face. Oliver laughed for the third time. "Stand back or you'll frighten the horse and he'll bolt," he said, as he jerked the reins and the cart rattled off out of the yard again.

Sarah stared after him, keeping her eyes on him until the cart was like a toy cart in the distance, with a toy horse under it, and Oliver himself a toy farmer made out of painted wood.

When Kathleen came home the following Friday her house was cleaner than it had ever been. The boards were scrubbed white as rope, the windows glinted and there was bread cooling on the sill. Kathleen paid Sarah and Sarah went home. Her brothers were glad to have her back to clean the house and make the beds and bake. She gave them her money. The children were glad to see her too because while she was away their uncles made them work all day footing turf and running after sheep like collie dogs.

Sarah worked hard as she had always done, for a few months. Then one night as she was handing round potato-cakes to her brothers and the children who were sitting around the kitchen table with their knives and forks at the ready in their hands, the elder brother Pat gave a sharp look at her. He poked Joseph, the younger brother, in the ribs with the handle of his knife. "For God's sake," he said, "will you look at her!"

Sarah ignored Pat's remark, except for a toss of her head. She sat down and ate her own supper greedily, swilling it down with several cups of boiling tea. When she'd finished she got up and went out into the wagon-blue night. Her brothers stared after her. "Holy God," Pat said, "something will have to be done about her this time."

"Ah what's the use of talking like that?" Joseph said, twitching his shoulders uneasily. "If the country is full of black-guards, what can we do about it?"

Pat put down his knife and fork and thumped the table with his closed fist.

"I thought the talking-to she got from the priest the last time would knock sense into her. The priest said a Home was the only place for the like of her. I told him we'd have no part in putting her away – God Almighty what would we do without her? There must be a woman in the house! – but we can't stand for much more of this."

Joseph was still pondering over the plight they'd be in without her. "Her brats need her too," he said, "leastways until they can be sent out to service themselves." He looked up. "That won't be long now though; they're shaping into fine strong boys."

But Pat stood up. "All the same something will have to be done. When the priest hears about this he'll be at me again. And this time I'll have to give him a better answer than the other times."

Joseph shrugged his shoulders. "Ah tell him you can get no rights of her. And isn't it the truth?" He gave an easy-going chuckle. "Tell him to tackle the job himself!"

Pat gave a sort of a laugh too but it was less easy. "Do you remember what he said the last time? He said if she didn't tell the name of the father, he'd make the new born infant open its mouth and name him."

"How well he didn't do it! Talk is easy!" Joseph said.

"He didn't do it," said Pat, "because Sarah took care not to let him catch sight of the child till the whole thing was put to the back of his mind by something else – the Confirmation – or the rewiring of the chapel."

"Well, can't she do the same with this one?" Joseph said. He stood up. "There's one good thing about the whole business, and that is that Mrs Kedrigan didn't notice anything wrong with her, or she'd never have given her an hour's work!"

Pat twitched with annoyance. "How could Mrs Kedrigan notice anything? Isn't it six months at least since she was working in Kedrigan's?"

"It is I suppose," Joseph said.

The two brothers moved about the kitchen for a few minutes in silence. The day with its solidarity of work and eating was over and they were about to go their separate ways when Joseph spoke.

"Pat?"

"What?"

"Oh nothing," said Joseph. "Nothing at all."

"Ah quit your hinting! What are you trying to say? Speak out man."

"I was only wondering," said Joseph. "Have you any idea at all who could be the father of this one?"

"Holy God," Pat cried in fury. "Why would you think I'd know the father of this one any more than the others? But if you think I'm going to stay here all evening gossiping like a woman, you're making a big mistake. I'm going out. I'm going over to the quarry field to see that heifer is all right that was sick this morning."

"Ah the heifer'll be all right," Joseph said. But feeling his older brother's eyes were on him he shrugged his shoulders. "You can give me a shout if she's in a bad way and you want me." Then when he'd let Pat get as far as the door he spoke again. "I won't say anything to her, I suppose, when she comes in?" he asked.

Pat swung around. "And what would you say, I'd like to know? Won't it be all beyond saying anyway in a few weeks when everyone in the countryside will see for themselves what's going on?"

"That's right," said Joseph.

Sarah went out every night, as she had always done, when dusk began to crouch over the fields. And her brothers kept silent tongues in their heads about the child she was carrying. She worked even better than before and she sang at her work. She carried the child deep in her body and she boldly faced an abashed congregation at Mass on Sundays, walking down the centre aisle and taking her usual place under the fourth station of the cross.

Meantime Mrs Kedrigan too was expecting her long-delayed child, but she didn't go to Mass: the priest came to her. She was looking bad. By day she crept from chair to chair around the kitchen, and only went out at night for a bit of a walk up and down their own lane. She was self-conscious about her condition and her nerves were frayed. Oliver used to have to sit up half the night with her and hold her moist hands in his until she fell asleep, but all the same she woke often and was frightened and peevish and, in bursts of hysteria, she called him a cruel brute. One evening she was taking a drop of tea by the fire. Oliver had gone down to the Post Office to see if there was a letter from the Maternity Hospital in Dublin, where she had engaged a bed for the following month. When he came back Oliver had a letter in his hand. Before he gave it to her, he told her what was in it. It was an anonymous letter and it named him as the father of the child Sarah Murray was going to bring into the world in a few weeks. He told Kathleen it was an unjust accusation.

"For God's sake, say something, Katty," he said. "You don't believe the bloody letter, do you?" Kathleen didn't answer. "You don't believe it, sure you don't." He went over to the window and laid his burning face against the cold pane of glass. "What will I do, Katty?"

"You'll do nothing," Kathleen said, speaking for the first time. "Nothing. Aren't you innocent? Take no notice of that letter."

She stooped and with a wide and grotesque swoop she plucked up the letter. Then she got to her feet and put the letter under a plate on the dresser and began to get the tea ready with slow, tedious journeyings back and forth across the silent kitchen. Oliver stood looking out at the fields until the tea was ready and once or twice he looked at his wife with curiosity. At last he turned away from the window and went over to the dresser. "I'll tear up the letter," he said.

"You'll do nothing of the kind," Kathleen said, and with a lurch she reached the dresser before him. "Here's where that letter belongs."

There was a sound of crackling and a paper-ball went into the heart of the flames. Oliver watched it burn, and although he thought it odd that he didn't see the writing on it, he still believed that it was Sarah's letter that coiled into a black spiral in the grate..

The next evening Sarah was sitting by the fire as Kathleen Kedrigan had been sitting by hers. She too was drinking a cup of tea, and she didn't look up when her brothers came into the kitchen. No one spoke, but after a minute or two Sarah went to get up to prepare the supper. Her brother Pat pushed her down again on the chair. The cup shattered against the range and the tea slopped over the floor.

"Is this letter yours? Did you write it?" he shouted at her, holding out a letter addressed to Oliver Kedrigan – a letter that had gone through the post, and been delivered and opened. "Do you hear me talking to you? Did you write this letter?"

"What business is it of yours?" Sarah said sullenly, and again she tried to get to her feet.

"Sit down, I tell you," Pat shouted, and he pressed her back. "Answer my question. Did you write this letter?"

Sarah stared dully at the letter in her brother's hand. The firelight flickered in her yellow eyes. "Give it to me," she snarled, and she snatched it from him. "What business is it of yours, you thief?"

"Did you hear that, Pat? She called you a thief!" the younger brother shouted.

"Shut up, you," Pat said. He turned back to his sister. "Answer me. Is it true what it says in this letter?"

"How do I know what it says! And what if it is true? It's no business of yours"

"I'll show you whose business it is!" Pat said. For a minute he stood as if not knowing what to do. Then he ran into the room off the kitchen where Sarah slept with the three children. He came out with an armful of clothes, a red dress, a coat, and a few bits of underwear. Sarah watched him. There was no one holding her down now but she didn't attempt to rise. Again her brother stood for a moment in the middle of the floor irresolute. Then he heard the outer door rattle in a gust of wind, and he ran towards it and dragging it open he threw out the armful of clothing, and ran back into the room. This time he came out with a jumper and a red cap, an alarm clock and a few other odds and ends. He threw them out the door, too.

"Do you know it's raining, Pat?" the younger brother asked cautiously.

"What do I care if it's raining?" Pat said. He went into the other room a third time. He was a while in there rummaging and when he came out he had a picture-frame, a prayer book, a pair of high-heeled shoes, a box of powder and a little green velvet box stuck all over with pearly shells.

Sarah sprang to her feet. "My green box. Oh! Give me my box!" She tried to snatch it from him.

But Joseph suddenly put out a foot and tripped her.

When Sarah got to her feet Pat was standing at the door throwing her things out one by one, but he kept the green box till last and when he threw it out he fired it with all his strength as far as it would go as if trying to reach the dunghill at the other end of the yard. At first Sarah made as if to run out to get the things back. Then she stopped and started to pull on her coat, but her brother caught her by the hair, at the same time pulling the coat off her. Then, by the hair he dragged her across the kitchen and pushed her out into the rain, where she slipped and fell again on the wet slab stone of the doorway. Quickly then he shut out the sight from his eyes by banging the door closed.

"That ought to teach her," he said. "Carrying on with a married man! No one is going to say I put up with that kind of thing. I didn't mind the other times when it was probably old Molloy or his like that would have been prepared to pay for his mistakes if the need arose, but I wasn't going to stand for a thing like this."

"You're sure it was Kedrigan?"

"Ah! didn't you see the letter yourself! Wasn't it Sarah's writing? And didn't Mrs Kedrigan herself give it to me this morning?"

"Sarah denied it, Pat," Joseph said. His spurt of courage had given out and his hands were shaking as he went to the window and pulled back a corner of the bleached and neatly-sewn square of a flour bag that served as a curtain.

"She did! And so did he, I suppose? Well, she can deny it somewhere else now."

"Where do you suppose she'll go?"

"She can go where she bloody well likes. And shut your

mouth, you. Keep away from that window! Can't you sit down? Sit down, I tell you."

All this took place at nine o'clock on a Tuesday night. The next morning at seven o'clock, Oliver Kedrigan went to a fair in a neighbouring town where he bought a new ram. He had had his breakfast in the town and he wanted to get on with his work, but he went to the door of the kitchen to see his wife was all right and called in to her from the yard. "Katty! Hand me the tin of raddle. It's on top of the dresser."

Kathleen Kedrigan came to the door and she had the tin of raddle in her hand.

"You won't be troubled with any more letters," she said.

Oliver laughed self-consciously. "That's a good thing, anyhow," he said. "Hurry, give me the raddle."

His wife held the tin in her hand, but she didn't move. She leaned against the jamb of the door. "I see you didn't hear the news?"

"What news?"

"Sarah Murray got what was coming to her last night. Her brothers turned her out of the house, and threw out all her things after her."

Oliver's face darkened.

"That was a cruel class of thing for brothers to do. Where did she go?"

"She went where she and her likes belong; into a ditch on the side of the road!"

Oliver said nothing. His wife watched him closely and she clenched her hands. "You can spare your sympathy. She won't need it."

Oliver looked up.

"Where did she go?"

"Nowhere," Kathleen said slowly.

Oliver tried to think clearly. It had been a bad night, wet and windy. "She wasn't out all night in the rain?" he asked, a fierce light coming into his eyes.

"She was," Kathleen said, and she stared at him. "At least that's where they found her in the morning, dead as a rat. And the child dead beside her!"

Her pale eyes held his, and he stared uncomprehendingly into them. Then he looked down at her hand that held the tin of red sheep-raddle.

"Give me the raddle!" he said, but before she had time to hand it to him he yelled at her again. "Give me the raddle. Give it to me. What are you waiting for? Give me the God-damn' stuff."

Peggy Seeger

I'm Gonna Be an Engineer

The words take some fitting into this skeletal tune, but if not sung too fast the song sings well.

Easily

When I was a lit-tle girl I wished I was a boy, I tagged a-long be-hind the gang and wore my cor-dur-oys, Eve-ry-bod-y said I on-ly did it to an-noy, But I was gon-na be an en-gi-neer.

Mom-ma told me 'Can't you be a la-dy? Your du-ty is to make me the moth-er of a pearl. Wait un-til you're old-er, dear, and may-be You'll be glad that you're a girl.'

(this part only after verses 1,3,6 and 7)

Dain-ty as a dres-den sta-tue, Gen-tle as a jer-sey cow; Smooth as silk, Gives cream-y milk: Learn to coo, Learn to moo, That's what it takes to be a lad-y now.

When I was a little girl I wished I was a boy,
I tagged along behind the gang and wore my corduroys,
Everybody said I only did it to annoy,
But I was gonna be an engineer.

Momma told me, "Can't you be a lady?
Your duty is to make me the mother of a pearl.
Wait until you're older, dear, and maybe
You'll be glad that you're a girl."

> *Dainty as a dresden statue,*
> *Gentle as a jersey cow*
> *Smooth as silk,*
> *Gives creamy milk:*
> *Learn to coo,*
> *Learn to moo,*
> *That's what it takes to be a lady now.*

When I went to school I learned to write and how to read,
Some history, geography and home economy,
And typing is a skill that every girl is sure to need
To while away the extra time until the time to breed,
And then they had the nerve to say, "What would you like to
    be?"
I says "I'm gonna be an engineer!"

No, you only need to learn to be a lady,
The duty isn't yours, for to try and run the world,
An engineer could never have a baby,
Remember, dear, that you're a girl.

So I become a typist and I study on the sly,
Working out the day and night so I can qualify,
And every time the boss come in he pinched me on the thigh,
Says, "I've never had an engineer!"

You owe it to the job to be a lady,
It's the duty of the staff for to give the boss a whirl,
The wages that you get are crummy, maybe,
But it's all you get cos you're a girl.

She's smart (for a woman)
I wonder how she got that way?
You get no choice,
You get no voice,
Just stay mum,
Pretend you're dumb,
That's how you come to be a lady today.

Then Jimmy come along and we set up a conjugation,
We were busy every night with loving recreation,
I spent my days at work so he could get his education,
And now he's an engineer!

He says, "I know you'll always be a lady
It's the duty of my darling to love me all her life,
Could an engineer look after or obey me?
Remember, dear, that you're my wife!"

As soon as Jimmy got a job I studied hard again,
Then, busy at me turret-lathe a year or so, and then
The morning that the twins were born, Jimmy says to them,
"Kids, your mother was an engineer."

You owe it to the kids to be a lady,
Dainty as a dish-rag, faithful as a chow.
Stay at home, you've got to mind the baby
Remember you're a mother now.

Every time I turn around there's something else to do,
Cook a meal or mend a sock or sweep a floor or two,
I listen in to Jimmy Young, it makes me want to spew,
I was gonna be an engineer.

I really wish that I could be a lady,
I could do the lovely things that a lady's s'posed to do.
I wouldn't mind if only they would pay me.
And I could be a person too.

What price – for a woman?
You can buy her for a ring of gold;
To love and obey
(Without any pay)
You get a cook or a nurse,
For better or worse,
You don't need a purse when a lady is sold.

But now that times are harder, and my Jimmy's got the sack,
I went down to Vickers, they were glad to have me back.
I'm a third-class citizen, my wages tell me that,
But I'm a first-class engineer.

The boss he says, "I pay you as a lady,
You only got the job cos I can't afford a man.
With you I keep the profits high as may be,
You're just a cheaper pair of hands."

You've got one fault: you're a woman,
You're not worth the equal pay.
A bitch or a tart,
You're nothing but heart,
Shallow and vain,
You got no brain,
Go down the drain like a lady today.

I listened to my mother and I joined a typing pool,
I listened to my lover and I sent him through his school,
If I listen to the boss, I'm just a bloody fool,
And an underpaid engineer.

I've been a sucker ever since I was a baby,
As a daughter, as a wife, as a mother and a dear,
But I'll fight them as a woman, not a lady,
I'll fight them as an engineer.

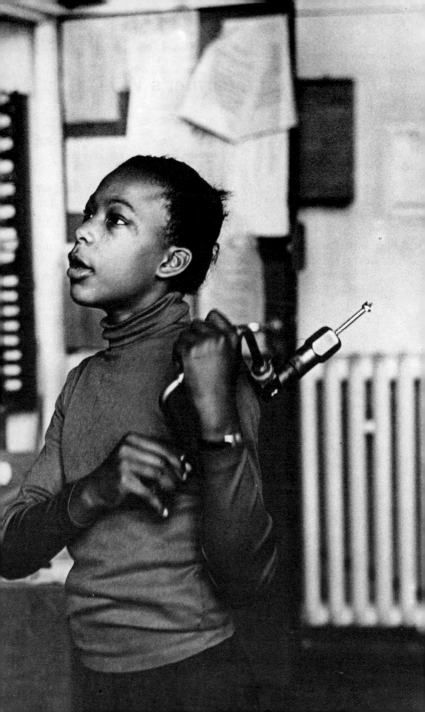

Anne Hughes

The Diary of a Farmer's Wife

Sept. ye 17. – We did hav divers folkes here to the meeting for the passon's hous. Farmer Bliss did say its verrie well, but where the hous? Whereone the butler from the big hous did say that my lord did offer Gunns Cott, and he to make all tidie, if John thinks propper; and sum chaires and ettcettera for the passon's use.

Then Mistress Prue did offer a bed and 2 chaires, and others offering, John will make up the reste from my lordes big hous. So it be settled, and John sayeing he did like much the young passon, they all say yes, he must cum. I be verrie glad for he is a nice lad.

I did talk to carters lad toe-daye, and did rate him soundlie for his bad treateing of Sarah, and giveing him a gret boxe of the eers, which did make him youpe, and bidden him to cum no more to the hous on paine of a horse whippen. I did make him worke verrie harde at divers jobbes till verrie glad when time for home did cum. I fear me if the new passon do cum to live here, he will wante my Sarah, bein verrie strucke with her as I could see. But I shall not stand in her way. She be a good maid and I like her much.

Sept. ye 19. – Carters wiffe cums for the scrubbing of the passidges and to the lime washeing of the dairy; and do tell me that old Tranter did go home in a woefull frite yester-night, sayeing that he cumming home at after dark did meet old Amos Courts ghoste; with a gret bigge black dogge, with eyes like saussers which did shoot fire. And that old Amos did grone much and did hit old Tranter with a gret bigge appel so that he hurt sum what. Carters wiffe do say she be skert to go nigh a orchard for fere of Old Amos, but I dout if old Tranters tale be true, knowing well his lying tongue. But I like not the talke of ghostes and such things. Mistress Prue cumming for her butter, I do tell her; at which she do laff hartilie, and do tell me not to caddel myself; that there be no such things as ghostes. So I do laff with her, albeit not feeling verrie sure.

Carters wiffe did say that Betsie Ann Arthers be in danger of lossinge her home threw bein sold up fur debte; she bein a verrie spendie wretch, and do save naught, yet do put on new gownes and bonnits, and so do waste her monies what she should put in her stockinge.

WEDDING INVITATION

Sept. ye 21. – Cum a man with a letter to say will we go to his dauter's wedding cum next Munday; and that Mary do wante Sarah, to be her maid. This I tell Sarah, who do saye, will I agree? To which I did, and did tell her I will dress her myself; at which she verrie pleesed.

Me telling the man to say Master Hughes and me will go if possibel, he off, after drinking a cup of cider and etting a lump of bred and ham.

So it do seem young Somers be wedding Mary after all. Butt I fere there will be verrie littel to start with. John in, I do tell him of the wedding, and what I did say back; and he quite reddie, if nothing ado to hinder. And so its setteld. Later cum Farmer Jones to say the young passon will do for Mary. John do saye he agree, so all be reddie.

SARAH DRESSES UP

Farmer Jones gone, John and me to talking what best to give Mary for a present, and John saying that the little blacke sowes pigges be reddie for the weening, he will give her 3, and what will I doe? Then I do saye she can have one of my linnen tabel clothes; to which John agrees. Then we out to the pigge feedeing, and later Sarah and me to the pressing of the clene clothes and aireinge it to put away, reddie to use.

Sept. ye 24. – Bein bussie, I hav not time to write in my book till now. John bein gone to the smithes shoppe, me to my littel booke.

The new passon be here for the wedding cum to-morrowe, and be gone out with John. His name be Godfrey Cross, a verrie prettie name. I fere me much that he be struck with Sarah, but hope not, for I wish not to lose a good maid.

After dinner she and me to my bedd chamber, to see for her

gowne out of the big cheste. Me takeing a prettie gowne of white silk with pink roses upon it, did bid her put it on; which she did, turneing about and about for me to see. She looked verrie fine. Then I did out with sum shoes with silver buckells, and a bonnitt of pink straw with white roses under, to set on the haire. She putting all on, did look rarelie; and so plessed was I that I did carry her to the best kitchen for John and passon to see. They did praise her mitilie, and I could see passon was verrie struck at such a prettie wench. Then we back up stayers agen to put away the finerie till to-morrowe, and Sarah did say with teares in her eyes how she did wish her mother could see her in her prettie cloes. I did say, howe good it would be; for I did know just how she did feel; for many a time I hav wished my own deer mother was here to see and hear this and that.

So after cumferting Sarah, we back to tee drinking; and me askeing John first, did bid Sarah to set at our tabel. Passon be slepeing here to night in the best bed chamber, on a verrie good fether bed my dear mother did make from her goose fether.

Sept. ye 26. – Yester morn we up betime to be reddie for Mary Jones wedding att 11 of the clocke. The sun didd shine and it were verrie warm. Carters wiffe cumming to help in good time we finish work erlie.

Then mee and Sarah upp to her bedd chamber, after me putting reddie Johns best velvet britches and blue silk stockeings with the purpel plusshe coate of my lordes with the gold lace, and his best shoes with two big golden buckles, and his best hat. Carters wiffe did praise Sarah much sayeing that she never in her born days did see such a daintie maid in all her finerie. Then I to my bedd chamber to put on my blue silk gown with the wide lace flounces of butter cullor; and shoes with the glass buckels, which were my dear ladies; and a blue straw bonnitt with the white ribbons; and did wear my red necklace which did look verrie fine.

Then me to help John into his britches, which he did get in to after much puffing and grunting; but indeed I was verrie proud when all reddie; and John, mighty proud to see me and Sarah lookeing so fine, did bid Carters wiffe to have a care not to over feed the black sowe and to be sure to strip the cows of all their milk. We off to the church in good time, John mighty proud to be in the cumpany of 2 such fine ladies, he did say, laffing at us.

A HEALTH TO THE BRIDE

Then mee not knowing if I had locked up the meat safe in the dairy, was about to turn about; but Sarah telling me she had done it herself, and put away turkey in the brown pot, I more content and into church, where were all the folk reddie who did stare at us with mouth agape as we did get to our seats; Sarah stopping with us till the wedding partie did cum. Mary did look verrie cumlie in her white gown with a fine lace kerchief; but my Sarah did out shine them all with her dark curlie hair and prettie pinke cheeks. A wedding be a verrie sollum thing, and not to be entered into lightlie; one do make sum verrie grate promisses which we must keep and not fail therein. I could not help but think how blest I was with my John at my side; albeit he be like a great baby at times with his show of temper. I did feel the dear God had bin good to me and my own life had fell in plessente places. The passon did read the service verrie well, and did give a good exortashun to end all. Then we all out and to the Ley Farm where we did find all reddie, so every body falling to did make a good meale; then John as becum the biggest farmer did say let us drink the brides helthe which every body did with much laffing at her blushes; then up gets Farmer Lewis from Blackmores to say lets drink to the 2 prettiest ladies in the place – Mistress Hughes and her maid Sarah; long life to both, at which I did stand up and say my thanks and say that Sarah was as good a maid as she was prettie, at which they did all shout agreement and fill their glasses.

FIDDLERS STRIKE UP

John was mighty pleased at all this; then old Timothy Martin did say if he was 50 years younger he should cum acourten Sarah, at which all did laffe and she blussh as red as a cherrie; but I did like her manners much, she being verrie modest and not putting her self forrad at all.

Then the fiddelers strikeing up a lively tune we to danceing rite reddie, after so much jigging about.

There were many cakes and divers things, but not baked to my mind a bit, me lykeing them verrie light, not lumpie. Later cum Mary and her man to thank me and John for our pressents which did please them both. Then we home not stopping for more danceing; and Sarah and the passon cuming with us, John did wispur that it would be a good thing for Sarah, and a step

71

up to be a passons wife. Att which I did tell him to stop it, me not wanting to lose Sarah; but I do see they be mighty good friends. We home to find all work done and Carters wiffe reddie for home, but I did bid her stop a while, knoweing she did want to hear all. So we to drink a cup of tea, and me telling her all about the wedding and giveing her 3 little cakes Mistress Jones had give Sarah for her. She was mighty pleased, and did say she sure no boddie did look finer than we, and that the master didd look as good a gentelman as my lord hiselfe; and she be right for John did look verrie fine in deed.

Then she home and me and Sarah up stairs to take off our finery. I did tell Sarah to put away her gown and hat and shoes in her own chest and to keep it for her own at which she did thank me verrie prettie and did put it over the bed rail to air, before putting it away. Then I to my chamber likewise to change clothes and down again, did go to the yards to see all well; then me and John and Passon did go to Gunns Cott to see how it does. It do look much nicer now and men be putting on a new roof; and John do say it must be called the passenage now. Then we home to supper which Sarah had all reddie for us, and to bed.

Sept. ye 28. – Yesterday we to the washeing and butter makeing. Carters wiffe here at 5 of the clock, we soon get all done and then to the makeing of pies and cakes; and also the makeing of a honey cake, bein Johns favourit cake.

HONEY-CAKE AND ROLLIES

I do make it thus: A lump of butter, a bigg cup of sugar, 3 eggs, a measure of swete plums, a measure of flour, and sum milk. I do beet the eggs and butter and sugar with a cup of honey till it be verrie frothie and bubbelie; then I do put in the flour and beet it again till verrie light, then I do throw in the swete plums and put all in a greased pan and bake in the bredd oven till it be cooked. This be a verrie prettie cake.

I did also make sum rollies, which be made by putting sum flour in a bowl then drop in 4 eggs and a bit of sugar and beet it up to a soft mess, then put in a long tin and bake gentlie. When it be cooked, I do turn it out gently on a board and put on sum swete plums and nut-meg and sprinkel with sugar, then roll it up and put away till cold.

JOHN BURNS HIS FINGERS

Later there came a poor boddie for sum bread to eat, a poor traipse of a woman with her clothes in rags and no shoes. I did give her a lump of bread and chesse and a cup of cider; she did ask for work, but I could not have a traipse about, and did say so. So she off for which I was verrie glad, not wishing John to think I do encourrage such; but I do always feel sorrie for them, me bein so much the better off. Then John cums in to say we must take the honey from the bees so he to the makeing of sulfur papers, which he do put near the fire. It flaring up, did burn his fingers: thereby he did drop all on my clene harthe stone, and did dance about like a bee in a bottel. I was verrie wroth at my harthe bein all messie, and did say it did serve him right for being such a great sillie. Weron he did say it be all our folte and to be plagued with a passel of women be enough to try any man.

I did put sum butter on his finger to stop the smarten theron, but he did make a mighty fuss. Sarah did scrape up the sulfur from the harthe stone and clene it, but it be stained and do smell verrie nastie; and I did tell John not to do it in my clene kitchen agen but in the washe hous, and did take all ther, bein crosse at the waste of good sulfur. Later Carters wiffe did cum and make a goodlie pile of the papers, and so we now all reddie to take the honey on to morrow.

Sept. ye 30. – We did have a bussie time takeing the honey from the bees yester night. Me and Sarah and Carters wiffe did have to do it all; John sayeing his fingers bein verrie sore from the burns.

Sarah did dig a big hole in the ground for each skeppe, where in we put a sulfur paper which we did set alight, and put the skeppes of bees on the topp. The smell of the sulfur do kill the bees, and so we do get the honey therfrom.

It do grief me to kill the poor things, bein such a waste of good bees, to lie in a great heep at the bottom of the hole when the skeppe be tooke of it; but we do want the honey, useing a gret lot in the hous for divers things.

CARTERS WIFFE AND THE BEES

Carters wiffe did fall backards and sat in a skeppe of bees, which did make a grett bussing and did send her youping out of the garden; at which Sarah did laff so hartilie, to see Carters wiffe holdeing up her gown while jumping over the cabbiges, that she did neerlie do the same thinge. At which I quite helpless to reprove her, laffing myeself at Carters wiffes spindlie, shankie legs a bobbin up and down among the vegitables. She back anon, with a mighty big nose where a bee had sat up on it, and we to the out hous with the honey skeppes there to leeve them till sure all the bees be gone. Then we shall brake the honey comb up and hit it all upp; and hang it up in a clene cotton bag to run it through; then we shall strain it divers times, and when clere put into the potts reddie to use. Then we shall make honey wine with the comb waxe; to 3 skeppes of wax we do put 2 big messures of water and boil all well till the wax do swim on the top.

WE MAKE HONEY WINE

This we do skim off and set aside; then we do put the liquor in a vat and while hot do put in it 6 lemons cut in pieces, 6 oringes, like wise 3 pieces of cinamon; then cover all with a clene cloth, and leave 3 days; then we do stur harde for 10 minets by the clock; and leave 3 days; and so on, till 12 days be past. Then strain verrie care-fully in to the cask and to each large messure [? 1 gallon] put 1 quart of best brandie and 3 dried clover blossoms and 1 egg shell broke in fine powder. Leave the bung out of the cask till the clover blows do work out on top of the cask, then bung down verrie tight, and keep a-while before tappeing. The wax we do boil many times till it be a nice yeller culler and no bits of black in it, when it can be stored to use for the pollishing and harness clening.

I can rite no more in my book today; John bein in the house, I fere he may see me.

Oct. ye 2. – Cousin Emmas lad here early with the news that Johns father be ill of a fit, and for John to go at once; so I to the packen of sum clothes not knowing how long he will be away, and he off after a lot of fusse and bother, riding Dobbin, so me left to see to all things.

ALARUMS FOR ANNE WHILE
JOHN IS AWAY

I be verrie sorry for John's mother, she be a dear soul and verrie kind to me when my deer mother died; that I love her much. Later me to the yards to set all going and to tell Carters wiffe to cum and slepe on the kitchen settel to gard us, she bein mighty brave and feering nought. Shepherd in later to say a sheep be cart and ded, and what shall he do with boddie? I tell him to take off the skin and do as he pleases with the rest; and I dout not he will have a feast as never was. But, la, he be welcum, not taisteing meet for many months.

The news spreading that John be gon, cums Mistress Prue to hear all about it. I do tell her all I do know, which be not much, but I do hope Emmas lad will cum soon and we know more.

Janice Elliot

Hymeneal

Susan Edden, just married, comes to the farm in 1921. Up the hill, but down in status, according to her mother, the doctor's wife. She has spent her life on the edge of, but never in farms. She comes up with Jesse ("Jesse," her mother says, "sounds like a girl. Is that a name for a man?") in the cart, not her father's car. Starting, she says, with a crispness that comes naturally to her, as she means to go on. But really because she fancies it.

Even outside the church, the two families keep to themselves. Eddens stiff and sweating in tight best suits; Aitkens moving easily in their clothes, capturing the vicar. Kisses, handkerchiefs, tears, some Aitken confetti, then suddenly, miraculously, from the Edden side great boughs and branches of orange blossom and lilac, spread at their feet, piled in the cart. Jesse swearing and blinking behind flowers. Joe, father Edden, missing, then up the road comes a flowering bush, swaying, almost a tree, all white. It seems a long time coming. The light shakes. Then, shedding some flowers, it is tumbled across their laps into the cart. And Joe colours and winks, first one eye, then the other, and just as embarrassing remarks and damp farewells seem inevitable, he thumps the mare, like a barmaid, on the backside, and she shivers, farts and leads off.

Someone has stuck cow-parsley in the mare's harness and hung two little bells on the reins. The white dusty blooms tickle her ears. It is a light cart. She trots and the bells ring. Between the village and the bare hill there is a natural avenue of bushes and trees. They move under white hawthorn, between high green, on their throne of boughs. Susan leans against her husband's shoulder. He puts an arm round her, leaving one hand for the reins.

"It was a lovely idea," she says, and when he seems not to understand: "the flowers." Inside her head her voice sounds artificial, patronizing. She would like to swallow her words, but no harm is done. He seems wrapped in some dream of his own.

He is a small, brown, slim man, his only weakness, it appears to her, a shyness at having snatched her from the arms of suitable young men. She must reassure him. She blesses, for once, her intelligence, which will find a way to convince him of her love, his own worth.

He grunts: "They'll want a do."

"Yes," she says, "of course. They'll expect it. For them."

"And you. It would be right."

"Oh, me. I don't care about things like that."

"You're a funny one." For the first time since they were married, half an hour ago, he really looks at her, puzzled and loving. "You know what you're in for? What you've lost?" He touches her cheek.

She laughs, clear-throated, easy. So that's what bothers him. "If you knew . . . how boring those people are. What you've saved me from."

"Perhaps."

"Hurry," she says, "hurry. I want to begin." They are out of the avenue and there is the hill and the house. She wants to throw open the windows, bring in flowers. The horse stops trotting and plods. "Make her go fast." She is excited and wants to tease him. "Or don't you whip mares?"

"Oh yes," he says. "They're all the same, beasts."

She likes to see him so sure with the reins. Something her father could not do. She congratulates herself on her instinct in choosing this man. She wishes only that she could spark off the same excitement in him. He kisses her softly on the cheek and touches the mare with the whip. They trot up the hill, shedding flowers.

The yard is smaller than she remembers, the ugly black barn bigger. A skinny dog runs out and barks at them. He sweats gently and it retreats, after a moment's doubt, wagging and cursing, making to its place under the barn.

"No," he says, "the front door."

They go through the side gate, stiff, never used, to the front of the house. He has to kick the hinge. Between the house and the hedge there is half an acre of freshly turned earth. He is proud of this and shy. She knows that she must look pleased, though it's hard to imagine, at this moment, what she might do with it. He points to the boundaries. He has spent every evening in the last month, from nine to eleven, digging.

"There! That's yours. Your garden." Anxious: "You like flowers? You said?"

"Yes," she says, and kisses him. "Thank you. I love it." Love, lovely, seem the only words she can say today. They don't mean much. They have been rubbed flat of meaning. But he doesn't notice. He uses words as the nearest tools that come to hand, rough and ready. Some fresher for his simplicity. She tells herself, I must go carefully; show him but not spoil him. She talks about roses and they go in.

She serves the cold chicken, puts away clothes and arranges her books. She can see how she might make this house her own, in time, with tact. Her mother caught her packing the books and said: "You'll have no time for them." "Then I'll make time."

"Your reading," he murmurs, touching their spines as if they held secrets. "I can hardly read more than my name."

"I'll teach you if you like."

"If there's time. Yes. I'd like that." He looks at her in wonder. "You're a queen, you know."

She smiles. She is entirely happy and convinced of the rightness of her choice. "But you too. You can do things I know nothing about. I'll be a fool, I know, on a farm. You'll have to show me."

"You'll learn."

After they have drunk tea (she would have preferred coffee but the tea, after all, tastes right) they go up. There is no electricity here, or gas. She is enchanted by the low roofed room and the oil lamps. She turns them down and waits in the dark. She thinks he will be shy. He smells of soap.

"You've shaved."

"Yes."

"Kiss me."

They have kissed often. This is familiar. She likes it, would like to prolong it. She feels very powerful, able to please him.

"Don't stop." He pauses, propped above her on one elbow. His voice is baffled, almost resentful.

"Why did you marry me?"

She refuses to take him seriously. "Now . . . let me see."

"Not my money or my looks." He is still solemn, quite stern. "Nor my reading. Was it a fancy?"

"Jesse! What do you think I am?"

"I think you're a clever young woman, who, if choice were

hers, would maybe never marry. Not as clever as you think. And you'd not be as content alone as you'll imagine, in bad times."

She is touched by his seriousness. "We'll have no bad times. I know it. Or none we can't overcome."

He seems not to have heard her.

"And you wanted to do something with yourself. You've got pride in yourself. But you didn't know what. Just that it had to be something the others don't do. You might have gone to one of those universities, been a teacher. But you fancied me."

"That's a terrible thing to say!" She is near to tears. They are whispering as if in Church. She had thought she held him, quiet and small, in the palm of her hand.

"No. For most that's what it comes down to, fancies. All I say is, Susan, don't build on me, not too much. That is, you can count on me always, I hope. But don't think I can be owt but myself."

"I don't understand!"

"It doesn't matter. It was best said now." He smiles and pulls her hands away from her eyes. Then he begins to laugh and romp like a young dog. He fools about, and kisses and tries to be gentle, but it still hurts, more than she could have believed possible. At once, he falls asleep. She lies awake, hurt and bewildered. He takes her once more in the night, without even opening his eyes. This time it is better. But her wedding night is not at all what she expected.

The next three days – a long weekend – are good. The farm is still small. It will grow in the next forty years, but now it is possible for Jesse to take a short holiday. Through the four-day honeymoon an Edden cousin and another man keep things going but avoid the house, averting their eyes as they follow their sloped shadows across the yard when, in the early morning, woken by unfamiliar farm noises, Susan appears at the window.

"There's Tam. I think I've shocked him."

He plunges his head in the bowl, pokes soap out of his ears.

"Not Tam. He thinks you're Queen of England."

"I'll show you what I think. Give me that towel."

"I might and I might not."

He lunges after her, blind with soap, groping. "You're a skinny cat."

She sidesteps. Wherever she goes, he follows, but slow,

threatening and swearing, roaring. It's like having a blind bull on a chain. They are behaving like children. This is the best time they will have.

"Give."

"Say I'm the Queen of England."

"I'm boggered if I will."

He pins her down at last and wipes his eyes on the sheet. These are silly, private jokes. Instinctively, from a sensibility with which she does not credit him, he gives her all the nonsense she wants, but does not know she wants. She may deny later, even to herself, that she has ever been so frivolous. She has gone into this marriage, she likes to think, with her eyes open, determined that it shall be good and lasting: she sees them as reasonable friends, teaching each other. He will learn to read, to listen to music (for which she feels he has a natural, if untutored ear); she to be a farmer's wife. Concerning the second project she is vague but optimistic. She has always been competent. As for his education, that will be a matter of tact and patience and love. Their marriage will be the richer – out of the ordinary – for these mutual benefits. She brings a great if invisible dowry and has a brain clear enough and a temperament cool enough ("Susan is such a *sensible* girl") to bestow it without offence or patronage. This is how her mind runs. She prizes her mind more than her looks. On one subject she might admit she is a romantic – common sense.

In these four days – after that first, odd night – her sensible resolutions are blurred by happiness. She notices, on the fourth day, that he is restless. His hands on the fine tablecloth (her mother's present) look foolish and empty. He wants to get back to work.

"You're worried about the farm?"

"The lambing's started. Tam's no shepherd. We can't afford to lose them."

"Shall we go and see?" She has noticed the pen in the sloping field behind the house, up in the corner, where the hedge makes a windbreak.

"You wouldn't mind?"

"I'd like to."

"You're a good girl."

"No. I'm just your wife. Besides –" she adds, with something of her natural airs, "I've never seen an animal born."

"It might be best if you stayed."

"No. I want to come. If I won't be in the way?"

"You," he says, and touches her cheek, "you."

They walk up the hill hand in hand. Up here there is a wind and the stars seem to be running, racing, falling. The couple pause for breath and look up:

"It's fine," he says.

"Yes. It's lovely. You know them?"

"No. Only the Plough." He jabs his thumb where the stars seem windiest. "And the Milky Way. Tam knows them. He's learned them from fishing." She knows what he means but likes to imagine Tam, sturdier and blacker than his cousin, monosyllabic, drawing in his trawling net great shoals of stars. She doesn't mention this. It sounds like the fancy of a silly girl. She frowns, as if dazzled, and says, offhand:

"It's strange to think some of them are dead. We're seeing them but they're not really there. You can think of space but not time. At least you can, but separately. Not time in space." Walking with her face tipped up she catches her ankle in a root. He holds her and they go up.

Tam has a lantern in the pen. A ewe lies on her side, apparently dead, but as they watch, the stomach, grossly extended between four skinny legs, heaves and flutters. The green eyes of the sheep, still open, seems to observe them. Tam nods:

"I was coming down. But by the time I found her she was near finished."

"She's gone?"

"Aye."

"When?" Jesse looks angry. For a second Susan thinks that he might strike Tam.

"Now. A minute. Two maybe."

"Knife."

Tam blinks. "You're going to cut her?"

Jesse has already flung off his coat and is kneeling. He nicks the ewe's belly, then remembers Susan:

"You'd better go back to the house."

"Can't I help?"

"It'll need feeding, if it lives, till we can find it a ewe. Warm some milk."

But she stays. Tam holds the lantern and she watches the two men, heads bent. She feels a fool, useless, but is too interested to leave. Then she is appalled as the womb is revealed and Jesse plunges his hands deep in like a woman in dough and pulls out the bloody mess. It's foul and marvellous. He's smiling. She stuffs her knuckles in her mouth and staggers outside to be sick. When she has finished she stays hunched, her cheek against the prickly black grass.

"I told you, get back to the house." His voice is rough. He keeps his soft face for the lamb. She follows him down the hill.

"How will you get another ewe to take it?"

"Find one with a dead lamb. Skin it. Put the skin on this 'un."

She stumbles but his arms are full with the lamb. She feels absurdly lonely, excluded, and then is ashamed of herself. Her voice sounds high and artificial:

"You did it so quickly. You seem to know just what to do."

"I'd better, it's my job."

"But I'd have no idea . . ."

"It's what you know. Nothing special. Like your reading."

"But that seems so pointless. It doesn't do anything for anyone but myself. It doesn't save a life."

"A life?" he says. "Don't go romancing about it. It's only a beast. I'd kill it as quick for money." But his face is slanted away from her, towards the sheep, now kicking in his arms. "You little bogger then, you want to run?" He sets it down and it wobbles in a circle back to him. "I'm not your mam." He picks it up again and now they're back at the farm. He says they'll keep it indoors for the night. It's sickly but should live. The honeymoon is over.

She stays outside for a moment in the yard. The racing sky makes the barn topple. There is a scent of hay and salt. She looks up, breasting the waves of darkness, to the high corner of the field where the stars are low and in the pen the lantern glows, a single small outpost of humanity in a scene suddenly cold and by no means benign. She shivers and goes indoors to warm the milk.

Fay Weldon

Weekend

By seven-thirty they were ready to go. Martha had everything packed into the car and the three children appropriately dressed and in the back seat, complete with educational games and wholewheat biscuits. When everything was ready in the car Martin would switch off the television, come downstairs, lock up the house, front and back, and take the wheel.

Weekend! Only two hours' drive down to the cottage on Friday evenings: three hours' drive back on Sunday nights. The pleasures of greenery and guests in between. They reckoned themselves fortunate, how fortunate!

On Fridays Martha would get home on the bus at six-twelve and prepare tea and sandwiches for the family: then she would strip four beds and put the sheets and quilt covers in the washing machine for Monday: take the country bedding from the airing basket, plus the books and the games, plus the weekend food – acquired at intervals throughout the week, to lessen the load – plus her own folder of work from the office, plus Martin's drawing materials (she was a market researcher in an advertising agency, he a freelance designer) plus hair-brushes, jeans, spare T-shirts, Jolyon's antibiotics (he suffered from sore throats), Jenny's recorder, Jasper's cassette player and so on – ah, the so on! – and would pack them all, skilfully and quickly, into the boot. Very little could be left in the cottage during the week. ("An open invitation to burglars": Martin.) Then Martha would run round the house tidying and wiping, doing this and that, finding the cat at one neighbour's and delivering it to another, while the others ate their tea; and would usually, proudly, have everything finished by the time they had eaten their fill. Martin would just catch the BBC2 news, while Martha cleared away the tea table, and the children tossed up for the best positions in the car. "Martha," said Martin, tonight, "you ought to get Mrs Hodder to do more. She takes advantage of you."

Mrs Hodder came in twice a week to clean. She was over seventy. She charged two pounds an hour. Martha paid her out of her own wages: well, the running of the house was Martha's concern. If Martha chose to go out to work – as was her perfect right, Martin allowed, even though it wasn't the best thing for the children, but that must be Martha's moral responsibility – Martha must surely pay her domestic stand-in. An evident truth, heard loud and clear and frequent in Martin's mouth and Martha's heart.

"I expect you're right," said Martha. She did not want to argue. Martin had had a long hard week, and now had to drive. Martha couldn't. Martha's licence had been suspended four months back for drunken driving. Everyone agreed that the suspension was unfair: Martha seldom drank to excess: she was for one thing usually too busy pouring drinks for other people or washing other people's glasses to get much inside herself. But Martin had taken her out to dinner on her birthday, as was his custom, and exhaustion and excitement mixed had made her imprudent, and before she knew where she was, why there she was, in the dock, with a distorted lamp-post to pay for and a new bonnet for the car and six months' suspension.

So now Martin had to drive her car down to the cottage, and he was always tired on Fridays, and hot and sleepy on Sundays, and every rattle and clank and bump in the engine she felt to be somehow her fault.

Martin had a little sports car for London and work: it could nip in and out of the traffic nicely: Martha's was an old estate car, with room for the children, picnic baskets, bedding, food, games, plants, drink, portable television and all the things required by the middle classes for weekends in the country. It lumbered rather than zipped and made Martin angry. He seldom spoke a harsh word, but Martha, after the fashion of wives, could detect his mood from what he did not say rather than what he did, and from the tilt of his head, and the way his crinkly, merry eyes seemed crinklier and merrier still – and of course from the way he addressed Martha's car.

"Come along, you old banger you! Can't you do better than that? You're too old, that's your trouble. Stop complaining. Always complaining, it's only a hill. You're too wide about the hips. You'll never get through there."

Martha worried about her age, her tendency to complain, and the width of her hips. She took the remarks personally. Was she

right to do so? The children noticed nothing: it was just funny lively laughing Daddy being witty about Mummy's car. Mummy, done for drunken driving. Mummy, with the roots of melancholy somewhere deep beneath the bustling, busy, everyday self. Busy: ah so busy!

Martin would only laugh if she said anything about the way he spoke to her car and warn her against paranoia. "Don't get like your mother, darling." Martha's mother had, towards the end, thought that people were plotting against her. Martha's mother had led a secluded, suspicious life, and made Martha's childhood a chilly and a lonely time. Life now, by comparison, was wonderful for Martha. People, children, houses, conversations, food, drink, theatres – even, now, a career. Martin standing between her and the hostility of the world – popular, easy, funny Martin, beckoning the rest of the world into earshot.

Ah, she was grateful: little earnest Martha, with her shy ways and her penchant for passing boring exams – how her life had blossomed out! Three children too – Jasper, Jenny and Jolyon – all with Martin's broad brow and open looks, and the confidence born of her love and care, and the work she had put into them since the dawning of their days.

Martin drives. Martha, for once, drowses.

The right food, the right words, the right play. Doctors for the tonsils: dentists for the molars. Confiscate guns: censor television: encourage creativity. Paints and paper to hand: books on the shelves: meetings with teachers. Music teachers. Dancing lessons. Parties. Friends to tea. School plays. Open days. Junior orchestra.

Martha is jolted awake. Traffic lights. Martin doesn't like Martha to sleep while he drives.

Clothes. Oh, clothes! Can't wear this: must wear that. Dress shops. Piles of clothes in corners: duly washed, but waiting to be ironed, waiting to be put away.

Get the piles off the floor, into the laundry baskets. Martin doesn't like a mess.

Creativity arises out of order, not chaos. Five years off work while the children were small: back to work with seniority lost. What, did you think something was for nothing? If you have children, mother, that is your reward. It lies not in the world.

Have you taken enough food? Always hard to judge.

Food. Oh, food! Shop in the lunch-hour. Lug it all home. Cook for the freezer on Wednesday evenings while Martin is at his car-maintenance evening class, and isn't there to notice you being unrestful. Martin likes you to sit down in the evenings. Fruit, meat, vegetables, flour for home-made bread. Well, shop bread is full of pollutants. Frozen food, even your own, loses flavour. Martin often remarks on it.

Condiments. Everyone loves mango chutney. But the expense!

London Airport to the left. Look, look, children! Concorde? No, idiot, of course it isn't Concorde.

Ah, to be all things to all people: children, husband, employer, friends! It can be done: yes, it can: super woman.

Drink. Home-made wine. Why not? Elderberries grown thick and rich in London: and at least you know what's in it. Store it in high cupboards: lots of room: up and down the step-ladder. Careful! Don't slip. Don't break anything.

No such thing as an accident. Accidents are Freudian slips: they are wilful, bad-tempered things.

Martin can't bear bad temper. Martin likes slim ladies. Diet. Martin rather likes his secretary. Diet. Martin admires slim legs and big bosoms. How to achieve them both? Impossible. But try, oh try, to be what you ought to be, not what you are. Inside and out.

Martin brings back flowers and chocolates: whisks Martha off for holiday weekends. Wonderful! The best husband in the world: look into his crinkly, merry, gentle eyes; see it there. So the mouth slopes away into something of a pout. Never mind. Gaze into the eyes. Love. It must be love. You married him. *You*. Surely *you* deserve true love?

Salisbury Plain. Stonehenge. Look, children, look! Mother, we've seen Stonehenge a hundred times. Go back to sleep.

Cook! Ah cook. People love to come to Martin and Martha's dinners. Work it out in your head in the lunch-hour. If you get in at six-twelve, you can seal the meat while you beat the egg white while you feed the cat while you lay the table while you string the beans while you set out the cheese, goat's cheese, Martin loves goat's cheese, Martha tries to like goat's cheese – oh, bed, sleep, peace, quiet.

Sex! Ah sex. Orgasm, please. Martin requires it. Well, so do you. And you don't want his secretary providing a passion you neglected to develop. Do you? Quick, quick, the cosmic bond. Love. Married love.

Secretary! Probably a vulgar suspicion: nothing more. Probably a fit of paranoics, à la mother, now dead and gone.

At peace.

R.I.P.

Chilly, lonely mother, following her suspicions where they led.

Nearly there, children. Nearly in paradise, nearly at the cottage. Have another biscuit.

Real roses round the door.

Roses. Prune, weed, spray, feed, pick. Avoid thorns. One of Martin's few harsh words.

"Martha, you can't not want roses! What kind of person am I married to? An anti-rose personality?"

Green grass. Oh, God, grass. Grass must be mown. Restful lawns, daisies bobbing, buttercups glowing. Roses and grass and books. Books.

Please, Martin, do we have to have the two hundred books, mostly twenties' first editions, bought at Christie's book sale on one of your afternoons off? Books need dusting.

Roars of laughter from Martin, Jasper, Jenny and Jolyon. Mummy says we shouldn't have the books: books need dusting!

Roses, green grass, books and peace.

Martha woke up with a start when they got to the cottage, and gave a little shriek which made them all laugh. Mummy's waking shriek, they called it.

Then there was the car to unpack and the beds to make up, and the electricity to connect, and the supper to make, and the cobwebs to remove, while Martin made the fire. Then supper – pork chops in sweet and sour sauce ("Pork is such a *dull* meat if you don't cook it properly": Martin), green salad from the garden, or such green salad as the rabbits had left ("Martha, did you really net them properly? Be honest, now!": Martin) and sauté potatoes. Mash is so stodgy and ordinary, and instant mash unthinkable. The children studied the night sky with the aid of their star map. Wonderful, rewarding children!

Then clear up the supper: set the dough to prove for the bread: Martin already in bed: exhausted by the drive and lighting the fire. ("Martha, we really ought to get the logs stacked properly. Get the children to do it, will you?": Martin.) Sweep and tidy: get the TV aerial right. Turn up Jasper's jeans where he has trodden the hem undone. ("He can't go around like *that*, Martha. Not even Jasper": Martin.)

Midnight. Good night. Weekend guests arriving in the

morning. Seven for lunch and dinner on Saturday. Seven for Sunday breakfast, nine for Sunday lunch. ("Don't fuss, darling. You always make such a fuss": Martin.) Oh, God, forgotten the garlic squeezer. That means ten minutes with the back of a spoon and salt. Well, who wants *lumps* of garlic? No one. Not Martin's guests. Martin said so. Sleep.

Colin and Katie. Colin is Martin's oldest friend. Katie is his new young wife. Janet, Colin's other, earlier wife, was Martha's friend. Janet was rather like Martha, quieter and duller than her husband. A nag and a drag, Martin rather thought, and said, and of course she'd let herself go, everyone agreed. No one exactly excused Colin for walking out, but you could see the temptation.

Katie versus Janet.

Katie was languid, beautiful and elegant. She drawled when she spoke. Her hands were expressive: her feet were little and female. She had no children.

Janet plodded round on very flat, rather large feet. There was something wrong with them. They turned out slightly when she walked. She had two children. She was, frankly, boring. But Martha liked her: when Janet came down to the cottage she would wash up. Not in the way that most guests washed up – washing dutifully and setting everything out on the draining board, but actually drying and putting away too. And Janet would wash the bath and get the children all sat down, with chairs for everyone, even the littlest, and keep them quiet and satisfied so the grown-ups – well, the men – could get on with their conversation and their jokes and their love of country weekends, while Janet stared into space, as if grateful for the rest, quite happy.

Janet would garden, too. Weed the strawberries, while the men went for their walk; her great feet standing firm and square and sometimes crushing a plant or so, but never mind, oh never mind. Lovely Janet; who understood.

Now Janet was gone and here was Katie.

Katie talked with the men and went for walks with the men, and moved her ashtray rather impatiently when Martha tried to clear the drinks round it.

Dishes were boring, Katie implied by her manner, and domesticity was boring, and anyone who bothered with that kind of thing was a fool. Like Martha. Ash should be allowed to stay where it was, even if it was in the butter, and conversations should never be interrupted.

Knock, knock. Katie and Colin arrived at one-fifteen on Saturday morning, just after Martha had got to bed. "You don't mind? It was the moonlight. We couldn't resist it. You should have seen Stonehenge! We didn't disturb you? Such early birds!"

Martha rustled up a quick meal of omelettes. Saturday nights' eggs. ("Martha makes a lovely omelette": Martin.) ("Honey, make one of your mushroom omelettes: cook the mushrooms separately, remember, with lemon. Otherwise the water from the mushrooms get into the egg, and spoils everything.") Sunday supper mushrooms. But ungracious to say anything.

Martin had revived wonderfully at the sight of Colin and Katie. He brought out the whisky bottle. Glasses. Ice. Jug for water. Wait. Wash up another sinkful, when they're finished. 2 a.m.

"Don't do it tonight, darling."

"It'll only take a sec." Bright smile, not a hint of self-pity. Self-pity can spoil everyone's weekend.

Martha knows that if breakfast for seven is to be manageable the sink must be cleared of dishes. A tricky meal, breakfast. Especially if bacon, eggs, and tomatoes must all be cooked in separate pans. ("Separate pans mean separate flavours!": Martin.)

She is running around in her nightie. Now if that had been Katie – but there's something so *practical* about Martha. Reassuring, mind; but the skimpy nightie and the broad rump and the thirty-eight years are all rather embarrassing. Martha can see it in Colin and Katie's eyes. Martin's too. Martha wishes she did not see so much in other people's eyes. Her mother did, too. Dear, dead mother. Did I misjudge you?

This was the second weekend Katie had been down with Colin but without Janet. Colin was a photographer: Katie had been his accessorizer. First Colin and Janet: then Colin, Janet and Katie: now Colin and Katie!

Katie weeded with rubber gloves on and pulled out pansies in mistake for weeds and laughed and laughed along with everyone when her mistake was pointed out to her, but the pansies died. Well, Colin had become with the years fairly rich and fairly famous, and what does a fairly rich and famous man want with a wife like Janet when Katie is at hand?

On the first of the Colin/Katie weekends Katie had appeared out of the bathroom. "I say," said Katie, holding out a damp towel with evident distaste, "I can only find this. No hope of a dry one?" And Martha had run to fetch a dry towel and amazingly found one, and handed it to Katie who flashed her a brilliant smile and said, "I can't bear damp towels. Anything in the world but damp towels," as if speaking to a servant in a time of shortage of staff, and took all the water so there was none left for Martha to wash up.

The trouble, of course, was drying anything at all in the cottage. There were no facilities for doing so, and Martin had a horror of clothes lines which might spoil the view. He toiled and moiled all week in the city simply to get a country view at the weekend. Ridiculous to spoil it by draping it with wet towels! But now Martha had bought more towels, so perhaps everyone could be satisfied. She would take nine damp towels back on Sunday evenings in a plastic bag and see to them in London.

On this Saturday morning, straight after breakfast, Katie went out to the car – she and Colin had a new Lamborghini; hard to imagine Katie in anything duller – and came back waving a new Yves St Laurent towel. "See! I brought my own, darlings."

They'd brought nothing else. No fruit, no meat, no vegetables, not even bread, certainly not a box of chocolates. They'd gone off to bed with alacrity, the night before, and the spare room rocked and heaved: well, who'd want to do washing-up when you could do that, but what about the children? Would they get confused? First Colin and Janet, now Colin and Katie?

Martha murmured something of her thoughts to Martin, who looked quite shocked. "Colin's my best friend. I don't expect him to bring anything," and Martha felt mean. "And good heavens, you can't protect the kids from sex for ever; don't be so prudish," so that Martha felt stupid as well. Mean, complaining, and stupid.

Janet had rung Martha during the week. The house had been sold over her head, and she and the children had been moved into a small flat. Katie was trying to persuade Colin to cut down on her allowance, Janet said.

"It does one no good to be materialistic," Katie confided. "I have nothing. No home, no family, no ties, no possessions.

Look at me! Only me and a suitcase of clothes." But Katie seemed highly satisfied with the me, and the clothes were stupendous. Katie drank a great deal and became funny. Everyone laughed, including Martha. Katie had been married twice. Martha marvelled at how someone could arrive in their mid-thirties with nothing at all to their name, neither husband, nor children, nor property and not mind.

Mind you, Martha could see the power of such helplessness. If Colin was all Katie had in the world, how could Colin abandon her? And to what? Where would she go? How would she live? Oh, clever Katie.

"My teacup's dirty," said Katie, and Martha ran to clean it, apologizing, and Martin raised his eyebrows, at Martha not Katie.

"I wish *you'd* wear scent," said Martin to Martha, reproachfully. Katie wore lots. Martha never seemed to have time to put any on, though Martin bought her bottle after bottle. Martha leapt out of bed each morning to meet some emergency – miaowing cat, coughing child, faulty alarm clock, postman's knock – when was Martha to put on scent? It annoyed Martin all the same. She ought to do more to charm him.

Colin looked handsome and harrowed and younger than Martin, though they were much the same age. "Youth's catching," said Martin in bed that night. "It's since he found Katie." Found, like some treasure. Discovered; something exciting and wonderful, in the dreary world of established spouses.

On Saturday morning Jasper trod on a piece of wood ("Martha, why isn't he wearing shoes? It's too bad.": Martin) and Martha took him into the hospital to have a nasty splinter removed. She left the cottage at ten and arrived back at one, and they were still sitting in the sun drinking, empty bottles glinting in the long grass. The grass hadn't been cut. Don't forget the bottles. Broken glass means more mornings at the hospital. Oh, don't fuss. Enjoy yourself. Like other people. Try.

But no potatoes peeled, no breakfast cleared, nothing. Cigarette ends still amongst old toast, bacon rind and marmalade. "You could have done the potatoes," Martha burst out. Oh, bad temper! Prime sin. They looked at her in amazement and dislike. Martin too.

"Goodness," said Katie. "Are we doing the whole Sunday

lunch bit on Saturday? Potatoes? Ages since I've eaten potatoes. Wonderful!"

"The children expect it," said Martha.

So they did. Saturday and Sunday lunch shone like reassuring beacons in their lives. Saturday lunch: family lunch: fish and chips. ("So much better cooked at home than bought": Martin.) Sunday. Usually roast beef, potatoes, peas, apple pie. Oh, of course. Yorkshire pudding. Always a problem with oven temperatures. When the beef's going slowly, the Yorkshire should be going fast. How to achieve that? Like big bosom and little hips.

"Just relax," said Martin. "I'll cook dinner, all in good time. Splinters always work their own way out: no need to have taken him to hospital. Let life drift over you, my love. Flow with the waves, that's the way."

And Martin flashed Martha a distant, spiritual smile. His hand lay on Katie's slim brown arm, with its many gold bands.

"Anyway, you do too much for the children," said Martin. "It isn't good for them. Have a drink."

So Martha perched uneasily on the step and had a glass of cider, and wondered how, if lunch was going to be late, she would get cleared up and the meat out of the marinade for the rather formal dinner that would be expected that evening. The marinaded lamb ought to cook for at least four hours in a low oven; and the cottage oven was very small, and you couldn't use that and the grill at the same time and Martin liked his fish grilled, not fried. Less cholesterol.

She didn't say as much. Domestic details like this were very boring, and any mild complaint was registered by Martin as a scene. And to make a scene was so ungrateful.

This was the life. Well, wasn't it? Smart friends in large cars and country living and drinks before lunch and roses and bird song – "Don't drink *too* much," said Martin, and told them about Martha's suspended driving licence.

The children were hungry so Martha opened them a can of beans and sausages and heated that up. ("Martha, do they have to eat that crap? Can't they wait?": Martin.)

Katie was hungry: she said so, to keep the children in face. She was lovely with children – most children. She did not particularly like Colin and Janet's children. She said so, and he accepted it. He only saw them once a month now, not once a week.

"Let me make lunch," Katie said to Martha. "You do so much, poor thing!"

And she pulled out of the fridge all the things Martha had put away for the next day's picnic lunch party – Camembert cheese and salad and salami and made a wonderful tomato salad in two minutes and opened the white wine – "not very cold, darling. Shouldn't it be chilling?" – and had it all on the table in five amazing competent minutes. "That's all we need, darling," said Martin. "You are funny with your fish-and-chip Saturdays! What could be nicer than this? Or simpler?"

Nothing, except there was Sunday's buffet lunch for nine gone, in place of Saturday's fish for six, and would the fish stretch? No. Katie had had quite a lot to drink. She pecked Martha on the forehead. "Funny little Martha," she said. "She reminds me of Janet. I really do like Janet." Colin did not want to be reminded of Janet, and said so. "Darling Janet's a fact of life," said Katie. "If you'd only think about her more, you might manage to pay her less." And she yawned and stretched her lean, childless body and smiled at Colin with her inviting, naughty little girl eyes, and Martin watched her in admiration.

Martha got up and left them and took a paint pot and put a coat of white gloss on the bathroom wall. The white surface pleased her. She was good at painting. She produced a smooth, even surface. Her legs throbbed. She feared she might be getting varicose veins.

Outside in the garden the children played badminton. They were bad-tempered, but relieved to be able to look up and see their mother working, as usual: making their lives for ever better and nicer: organizing, planning, thinking ahead, side-stepping disaster, making preparations, like a mother hen, fussing and irritating: part of the natural boring scenery of the world.

On Saturday night Katie went to bed early: she rose from her chair and stretched and yawned and poked her head into the kitchen where Martha was washing saucepans. Colin had cleared the table and Katie had folded the napkins into pretty creases, while Martin blew at the fire, to make it bright. "Good night," said Katie.

Katie appeared three minutes later, reproachfully holding out her Yves St Laurent towel, sopping wet. "Oh dear," cried Martha. "Jenny must have washed her hair!" And Martha was obliged to rout Jenny out of bed to rebuke her, publicly, if only to demonstrate that she knew what was right and proper. That meant Jenny would sulk all weekend, and that meant a treat or an outing mid-week, or else by the following week she'd be having an asthma attack. "You fuss the children too much," said Martin. "That's why Jenny has asthma." Jenny was pleasant enough to look at, but not stunning. Perhaps she was a disappointment to her father? Martin would never say so, but Martha feared he thought so.

An egg and an orange each child, each day. Then nothing too bad would go wrong. And it hadn't. The asthma was very mild. A calm, tranquil environment, the doctor said. Ah, smile, Martha smile. Domestic happiness depends on you. 21×52 oranges a year. Each one to be purchased, carried, peeled and washed up after. And what about potatoes. 12×52 pounds a year? Martin liked his potatoes carefully peeled. He couldn't bear to find little cores of black in the mouthful. ("Well, it isn't very nice, is it?": Martin.)

Martha dreamt she was eating coal, by handfuls, and liking it.

Saturday night. Martin made love to Martha three times. Three times? How virile he was, and clearly turned on by the sounds from the spare room. Martin said he loved her. Martin always did. He was a courteous lover; he knew the importance of foreplay. So did Martha. Three times.

Ah, sleep. Jolyon had a nightmare. Jenny was woken by a moth. Martin slept through everything. Martha pottered about the house in the night. There was a moon. She sat at the window and stared out into the summer night for five minutes, and was at peace, and then went back to bed because she ought to be fresh for the morning.

But she wasn't. She slept late. The others went out for a walk. They'd left a note, a considerate note: "Didn't wake you. You looked tired. Had a cold breakfast so as not to make too much mess. Leave everything 'til we get back." But it was ten o'clock, and guests were coming at noon, so she cleared away the bread, the butter, the crumbs, the smears, the jam, the spoons, the spilt sugar, the cereal, the milk (sour by now) and the dirty plates, and swept the floors, and tidied up quickly, and grabbed a cup of coffee, and prepared to make a rice and fish dish, and a chocolate mousse and sat down in the middle to eat a lot of bread and jam herself. Broad hips. She remembered the office work in her file and knew she wouldn't be able to do it. Martin anyway thought it was ridiculous for her to bring work back at the weekends. "It's your holiday," he'd say. "Why should they impose?" Martha loved her work. She didn't have to smile at it. She just did it.

Katie came back upset and crying. She sat in the kitchen while Martha worked and drank glass after glass of gin and bitter lemon. Katie liked ice and lemon in gin. Martha paid for all the drink out of her wages. It was part of the deal between her and Martin – the contract by which she went out to work. All things to cheer the spirit, otherwise depressed by a working wife and mother, were to be paid for by Martha. Drink, holidays, petrol, outings, puddings, electricity, heating: it was quite a joke between them. It didn't really make any difference: it was their joint money, after all. Amazing how Martha's wages were creeping up, almost to the level of Martin's. One day they would overtake. Then what?

Work, honestly, was a piece of cake.

Anyway, poor Katie was crying. Colin, she'd discovered, kept a photograph of Janet and the children in his wallet. "He's not free of her. He pretends he is, but he isn't. She has him by a stranglehold. It's the kids. His bloody kids. Moaning Mary and that little creep Joanna. It's all he thinks about. I'm nobody."

But Katie didn't believe it. She knew she was somebody all right. Colin came in, in a fury. He took out the photograph and set fire to it, bitterly, with a match. Up in smoke they went. Mary and Joanna and Janet. The ashes fell on the floor. (Martha swept them up when Colin and Katie had gone. It hardly seemed polite to do so when they were still there.) "Go back to her," Katie said. "Go back to her. I don't care. Honestly, I'd rather be on my own. You're a nice old fashioned thing. Run along then. Do your thing, I'll do mine. Who cares?"

"Christ, Katie, the fuss! She only just happens to be in the photograph. She's not there on purpose to annoy. And I do feel bad about her. She's been having a hard time."

"And haven't you, Colin? She twists a pretty knife, I can tell you. Don't you have rights too? Not to mention me. Is a little loyalty too much to expect?"

They were reconciled before lunch, up in the spare room. Harry and Beryl Elder arrived at twelve-thirty. Harry didn't like to hurry on Sundays; Beryl was flustered with apologies for their lateness. They'd brought artichokes from their garden. "Wonderful," cried Martin. "Fruits of the earth? Let's have a wonderful soup! Don't fret, Martha. I'll do it."

"Don't fret." Martha clearly hadn't been smiling enough. She was in danger, Martin implied, of ruining everyone's weekend. There was an emergency in the garden very shortly – an elm tree which had probably got Dutch elm disease – and Martha finished the artichokes. The lid flew off the blender and there was artichoke purée everywhere. "Let's have lunch outside," said Colin. "Less work for Martha."

Martin frowned at Martha: he thought the appearance of martyrdom in the face of guests to be an unforgivable offence.

Everyone happily joined in taking the furniture out, but it was Martha's experience that nobody ever helped to bring it in again. Jolyon was stung by a wasp. Jasper sneezed and sneezed from hay fever and couldn't find the tissues and he wouldn't use loo paper. ("Surely you remembered the tissues, darling?": Martin.)

Beryl Elder was nice. "Wonderful to eat out," she said, fetching the cream for her pudding, while Martha fished a fly from the liquefying Brie ("You shouldn't have bought it so ripe, Martha": Martin) – "except it's just some other woman has to do it. But at least it isn't *me*." Beryl worked too, as a secretary, to send the boys to boarding school, where she'd rather they weren't. But her husband was from a rather grand family, and she'd been only a typist when he married her, so her life was a mass of amends, one way or another. Harry had lately opted out of the stockbroking rat race and become an artist, choosing integrity rather than money, but that choice was his alone and couldn't of course be inflicted on the boys.

Katie found the fish and rice dish rather strange, toyed at it with her fork, and talked about Italian restaurants she knew. Martin lay back soaking in the sun: crying, "Oh, this is the life." He made coffee, nobly, and the lid flew off the grinder and there were coffee beans all over the kitchen especially in amongst the row of cookery books which Martin gave Martha Christmas by Christmas. At least they didn't have to be brought back every weekend. ("The burglars won't have the sense to steal those": Martin.)

Beryl fell asleep and Katie watched her, quizzically. Beryl's mouth was open and she had a lot of fillings, and her ankles were thick and her waist was going, and she didn't look after herself. "I love women," sighed Katie. "They look so wonderful asleep. I wish I could be an earth mother."

Beryl woke with a start and nagged her husband into going

home, which he clearly didn't want to do, so didn't. Beryl thought she had to get back because his mother was coming round later. Nonsense! Then Beryl tried to stop Harry drinking more home-made wine and was laughed at by everyone. He was driving, Beryl couldn't, and he did have a nasty scar on his temple from a previous road accident. Never mind.

"She does come on strong, poor soul," laughed Katie when they'd finally gone. "I'm never going to get married," – and Colin looked at her yearningly because he wanted to marry her more than anything in the world, and Martha cleared the coffee cups.

"Oh don't *do* that," said Katie, "do just sit *down*, Martha, you make us all feel bad," and Martin glared at Martha who sat down and Jenny called out for her and Martha went upstairs and Jenny had started her first period and Martha cried and cried and knew she must stop because this must be a joyous occasion for Jenny or her whole future would be blighted, but for once, Martha couldn't.

Her daughter Jenny: wife, mother, friend.

Mary E Wilkins Freeman

Louisa

"I don't see what kind of ideas you've got in your head, for my part." Mrs Britton looked sharply at her daughter Louisa, but she got no response.

Louisa sat in one of the kitchen chairs close to the door. She had dropped into it when she first entered. Her hands were all brown and grimy with garden-mould; it clung to the bottom of her old dress and her coarse shoes.

Mrs Britton, sitting opposite by the window, waited, looking at her. Suddenly Louisa's silence seemed to strike her mother's will with an electric shock; she recoiled, with an angry jerk of her head. "You don't know nothin' about it. You'd like him well enough after you was married to him," said she, as if in answer to an argument.

Louisa's face looked fairly dull; her obstinacy seemed to cast a film over it. Her eyelids were cast down; she leaned her head back against the wall.

"Sit there like a stick if you want to!" cried her mother.

Louisa got up. As she stirred, a faint earthy odor diffused itself through the room. It was like a breath from a ploughed field.

Mrs Britton's little sallow face contracted more forcibly. "I s'pose now you're goin' back to your potater patch," said she. "Plantin' potaters out there jest like a man, for all the neighbors to see. Pretty sight, I call it."

"If they don't like it, they needn't look," returned Louisa. She spoke quite evenly. Her young back was stiff with bending over the potatoes, but she straightened it rigorously. She pulled her old hat farther over her eyes.

There was a shuffling sound outside the door and a fumble at the latch. It opened, and an old man came in, scraping his feet heavily over the threshold. He carried an old basket.

"What you got in that basket, father?" asked Mrs Britton.

The old man looked at her. His old face had the round outlines and naive grin of a child.

"Father, what you got in that basket?"

Louisa peered apprehensively into the basket. "Where did you get those potatoes, grandfather?" said she.

"Digged 'em." The old man's grin deepened. He chuckled hoarsely.

"Well, I'll give up if he ain't been an' dug up all them potaters you've been plantin'!" said Mrs Britton.

"Yes, he has," said Louisa, "Oh, grandfather, didn't you know I'd jest planted those potatoes?"

The old man fastened his bleared blue eyes on her face, and still grinned.

"Didn't you know better, grandfather?" she asked again.

But the old man only chuckled. He was so old that he had come back into the mystery of childhood. His motives were hidden and inscrutable; his amalgamation with the human race was so much weaker.

"Land sakes! don't waste no more time talkin' to him," said Mrs Britton. "You can't make out whether he knows what he's doin' or not. I've give it up. Father, you jest set them partaters down, and you come over here an' set down in the rockin'-chair; you've done about 'nough work to-day."

The old man shook his head with slow mutiny.

"Come right over here."

Louisa pulled at the basket of potatoes. "Let me have 'em, grandfather," said she. "I've got to have 'em."

The old man resisted. His grin disappeared, and he set his mouth. Mrs Britton got up, with a determined air, and went over to him. She was a sickly, frail-looking woman, but the voice came firm, with deep bass tones, from her little lean throat.

"Now, father," said she, "you jest give her that basket, an' you walk across the room, and you set down in that rockin'-chair."

The old man looked down into her little pale, wedge-shaped face. His grasp on the basket weakened. Louisa pulled it away, and pushed past out of the door, and the old man followed his daughter sullenly across the room to the rocking-chair.

The Brittons did not have a large potato field; they had only an acre of land in all. Louisa had planted two thirds of her potatoes: now she had to plant them all over again. She had gone to the house for a drink of water; her mother had detained her, and in the meantime the old man had undone her work. She began putting the cut potatoes back in the ground. She was careful and laborious about it. A strong wind, full of moisture, was blowing from the east. The smell of the sea was in it, although this was some miles inland. Louisa's brown calico skirt blew out in it like a sail. It beat her in the face when she raised her head.

"I've got to get these in to-day somehow," she muttered. "It'll rain to-morrow."

She worked as fast as she could, and the afternoon wore on. About five o'clock she happened to glance at the road – the potato field lay beside it – and she saw Jonathan Nye driving past with his gray horse and buggy. She turned her back to the road quickly, and listened until the rattle of the wheels died away. At six o'clock her mother looked out of the kitchen window and called her to supper.

"I'm comin' in a minute," Louisa shouted back. Then she worked faster than ever. At half-past six she went into the house, and the potatoes were all in the ground.

"Why didn't you come when I called you?" asked her mother.

"I had to get the potatoes in."

"I guess you wa'n't bound to get 'em all in to-night. It's kind of discouragin' when you work, an' get supper all ready, to have it stan' an hour, I call it. An' you've worked 'bout long enough for one day out in this damp wind, I should say."

Louisa washed her hands and face at the kitchen sink, and smoothed her hair at the little glass over it. She had wet her hair too, and made it look darker: it was quite a light brown. She brushed it in smooth straight lines back from her temples. Her whole face had a clear bright look from being exposed to the moist wind. She noticed it herself, and gave her head a little conscious turn.

When she sat down to the table her mother looked at her with admiration, which she veiled with disapproval.

"Jest look at your face," said she; "red as a beet. You'll be a pretty-lookin' sight before the summer's out, at this rate."

Louisa thought to herself that the light was not very strong, and the glass must have flattered her. She could not look as well as she had imagined. She spread some butter on her bread very sparsely. There was nothing for supper but some bread and butter and weak tea, though the old man had his dish of Indian-meal porridge. He could not eat much solid food. The porridge was covered with milk and molasses. He bent low over it, and ate large spoonfuls with loud noises. His daughter had tied a towel around his neck as she would have tied a pinafore on a child. She had also spread a towel over the table-cloth in front of him, and she watched him sharply lest he should spill his food.

"I wish I could have somethin' to eat that I could relish the way he does that porridge and molasses," said she. She had scarcely tasted anything. She sipped her weak tea laboriously.

Louisa looked across at her mother's meagre little figure in its neat old dress, at her poor small head bending over the tea-cup, showing the wide parting in the thin hair.

"Why don't you toast your bread, mother?" said she. "I'll toast it for you."

"No, I don't want it. I'd jest as soon have it this way as any. I don't want no bread, nohow. I want somethin' to relish – a herrin', or a little mite of cold meat, or somethin'. I s'pose I could eat as well as anybody if I had as much as some folks have. Mis' Mitchell was sayin' the other day that she didn't believe but what they had butcher's meat up to Mis' Nye's every day in the week. She said Jonathan he went to Wolfsborough and brought home great pieces in a market-basket every week. I guess they have everything."

Louisa was not eating much herself, but now she took another slice of bread with a resolute air. "I guess some folks would be thankful to get this," said she.

"Yes, I s'pose we'd ought to be thankful for enough to keep us alive, anybody takes so much comfort livin'," returned her mother, with a tragic bitterness that sat oddly upon her, as she was so small and feeble. Her face worked and strained under the stress of emotion; her eyes were full of tears; she sipped her tea fiercely.

"There's some sugar," said Louisa. "We might have had a little cake."

The old man caught the word. "Cake?" he mumbled, with pleased inquiry, looking up, and extending his grasping old hand.

"I guess we ain't got no sugar to waste in cake," returned Mrs Britton. "Eat your porridge, father, an' stop teasin'. There ain't no cake."

After supper Louisa cleared away the dishes; then she put on her shawl and hat.

"Where you goin'?" asked her mother.

"Down to the store."

"What for?"

"The oil's out. There wasn't enough to fill the lamps this mornin'. I ain't had a chance to get it before."

It was nearly dark. The mist was so heavy it was almost rain. Louisa went swiftly down the road with the oil-can. It was a half-mile to the store where the few staples were kept that sufficed the simple folk in this little settlement. She was gone a half-hour. When she returned, she had besides the oil-can a package under her arm. She went into the kitchen and set them down. The old man was asleep in the rocking-chair. She heard voices in the adjoining room. She frowned, and stood still, listening.

"Louisa!" called her mother. Her voice was sweet, and higher pitched than usual. She sounded the *i* in Louisa long.

"What say?"

"Come in here after you've taken your things off."

Louisa knew that Jonathan Nye was in the sitting-room. She flung off her hat and shawl. Her old dress was damp, and had still some earth stains on it; her hair was roughened by the wind, but she would not look again in the glass; she went into the sitting-room just as she was.

"It's Mr Nye, Louisa," said her mother, with effusion.

"Good-evenin', Mr Nye," said Louisa.

Jonathan Nye half arose and extended his hand, but she did not notice it. She sat down peremptorily in a chair at the other side of the room. Jonathan had the one rocking-chair; Mrs Britton's frail little body was poised anxiously on the hard rounded top of the carpet-covered lounge. She looked at Louisa's dress and hair, and her eyes were stony with disapproval, but her lips still smirked, and she kept her voice sweet. She pointed to a glass dish on the table.

"See what Mr Nye has brought us over, Louisa," said she.

Louisa looked indifferently at the dish.

"It's honey," said her mother, "some of his own bees made it. Don't you want to get a dish an' taste of it? One of them little glass sauce dishes."

"No, I guess not," replied Louisa. "I never cared much about honey. Grandfather'll like it."

The smile vanished momentarily from Mrs Britton's lips, but she recovered herself. She arose and went across the room to the china closet. Her set of china dishes was on the top shelves, the lower were filled with books and papers. "I've got somethin' to show you, Mr Nye," said she.

This was scarcely more than a hamlet, but it was incorporated, and had its town books. She brought forth a pile of them, and laid them on the table beside Jonathan Nye. "There," said she, "I thought mebbe you'd like to look at these." She opened one and pointed to the school report. This mother could not display her daughter's accomplishment to attract a suitor, for she had none. Louisa did not own a piano or organ; she could not paint; but she had taught school acceptably for eight years – ever since she was sixteen – and in every one of the town books was testimonial to that effect, intermixed with glowing eulogy. Jonathan Nye looked soberly through the books; he was a slow reader. He was a few years older than Louisa, tall and clumsy, long-featured and long-necked. His face was a deep red with embarrassment, and it contrasted oddly with his stiff dignity of demeanor.

Mrs Britton drew a chair close to him while he read. "You see, Louisa taught that school for eight year," said she; "an' she'd be teachin' it now if Mr Mosely's daughter hadn't grown up an' wanted somethin' to do, an' he put her in. He was committee, you know. I dun' know as I'd ought to say so, an' I wouldn't want you to repeat it, but they do say Ida Mosely don't give very good satisfaction, an' I guess she won't have no reports like these in the town books unless her father writes 'em. See this one."

Jonathan Nye pondered over the fulsome testimony to Louisa's capability, general worth, and amiability, while she sat in sulky silence at the farther corner of the room. Once in a while her mother, after a furtive glance at Jonathan, engrossed in a town book, would look at her and gesticulate fiercely for her to come over, but she did not stir. Her eyes were dull and quiet, her mouth closely shut; she looked homely. Louisa was very pretty when pleased and animated, at other times she had a look like a closed flower. One could see no prettiness in her.

Jonathan Nye read all the school reports; then he arose heavily. "They're real good," said he. He glanced at Louisa and tried to smile; his blushes deepened.

"Now don't be in a hurry," said Mrs Britton.

"I guess I'd better be goin'; mother's alone."

"She won't be afraid; it's jest on the edge of the evenin'."

"I don't know as she will. But I guess I'd better be goin'." He looked hesitatingly at Louisa.

She arose and stood with an indifferent air.

"You'd better set down again," said Mrs Britton.

"No; I guess I'd better be goin'." Jonathan turned towards Louisa. "Good-evenin'," said he.

"Good-evenin'."

Mrs Britton followed him to the door. She looked back and beckoned imperiously to Louisa, but she stood still. "Now come again, do," Mrs Britton said to the departing caller. "Run in any time; we're real lonesome evenin's. Father he sets an' sleeps in his chair, an' Louisa an' me often wish somebody'd drop in; folks round here ain't none too neighborly. Come in any time you happen to feel like it, an' we'll both of us be glad to see you. Tell your mother I'll send home that dish to-morrow, an' we shall have a real feast off that beautiful honey."

When Mrs Britton had fairly shut the outer door upon Jonathan Nye, she came back into the sitting-room as if her anger had a propelling power like steam upon her body.

"Now, Louisa Britton," said she, "you'd ought to be ashamed of yourself – ashamed of yourself! You've treated him like a – hog!"

"I couldn't help it."

"Couldn't help it! I guess you could treat anybody decent if you tried. I never saw such actions! I guess you needn't be afraid of him. I guess he ain't so set on you that he means to ketch you up an' run off. There's other girls in town full as good as you an' better-lookin'. Why didn't you go an' put on your other dress? Comin' into the room with that old thing on, an' your hair all in a frowse! I guess he won't want to come again."

"I hope he won't," said Louisa, under her breath. She was trembling all over.

"What say?"

"Nothin'."

"I shouldn't think you'd want to say anything, treatin' him that way, when he came over and brought all that beautiful honey! He was all dressed up, too. He had on a real nice coat – cloth jest as fine as it could be, an' it was kinder damp when he come in. Then he dressed all up to come over here this rainy night an' bring this honey." Mrs Britton snatched the dish of honey and scudded into the kitchen with it. "Sayin' you didn't like honey after he took all that pains to bring it over!" said she.

"I'd said I liked it if I'd lied up hill and down." She set the dish in the pantry. "What in creation smells so kinder strong an' smoky in here?" said she, sharply.

"I guess it's the herrin'. I got two or three down to the store."

"I'd like to know what you got herrin' for?"

"I thought maybe you'd relish 'em."

"I don't want no herrin's, now we've got this honey. But I don't know that you've got money to throw away." She shook the old man by the stove into partial wakefulness, and steered him into his little bedroom off the kitchen. She herself slept in one off the sitting-rooms; Louisa's room was up-stairs.

Louisa lighted her candle and went to bed, her mother's scolding voice pursuing her like a wrathful spirit. She cried when she was in bed in the dark, but she soon went to sleep. She was too healthfully tired with her out-door work not to. All her young bones ached with the strain of manual labor as they had ached many a time this last year since she had lost her school.

The Brittons had been and were in sore straits. All they had in the world was this little house with the acre of land. Louisa's meagre school money had bought their food and clothing since her father died. Now it was almost starvation for them. Louisa was struggling to wrest a little sustenance from their stony acre of land, toiling like a European peasant woman, sacrificing her New England dignity. Lately she had herself split up a cord of wood which she had bought of a neighbor, paying for it in instalments with work for his wife.

"Think of a school-teacher goin' into Mis' Mitchell's house to help clean!" said her mother.

She, although she had been of poor, hard-working people all her life, with the humblest surroundings, was a born aristocrat, with that fiercest and most bigoted aristocracy which sometimes arises from independent poverty. She had the feeling of a queen for a princess of the blood about her school-teacher daughter; her working in a neighbor's kitchen was as galling and terrible to her. The projected marriage with Jonathan Nye was like a royal alliance for the good of the state. Jonathan Nye was the only eligible young man in the place; he was the largest land-owner; he had the best house. There were only himself and his mother; after her death the property would all be his. Mrs Nye was an older woman than Mrs Britton, who forgot her own frailty in calculating their chances of life.

"Mis' Nye is considerable over seventy," she said often to herself; "an' then Jonathan will have it all."

She saw herself installed in that large white house as reigning dowager. All the obstacle was Louisa's obstinacy, which her mother could not understand. She could see no fault in Jonathan Nye. So far as absolute approval went, she herself was in love with him. There was no more sense, to her mind, in Louisa's refusing him than there would have been in a princess refusing the fairy prince and spoiling the story.

"I'd like to know what you've got against him," she said often to Louisa.

"I ain't got anything against him."

"Why don't you treat him different, then, I want to know?"

"I don't like him." Louisa said "like" shamefacedly, for she meant love, and dared not to say it.

"*Like!* Well, I don't know nothin' about such likin's as some pretend to, an' I don't want to. If I see anybody is good an' worthy, I like 'em, an' that's all there is about it."

"I don't – believe that's the way you felt about – father," said Louisa, softly, her young face flushed red.

"Yes, it was. I had some common-sense about it."

And Mrs Britton believed it. Many hard middle-aged years lay between her and her own love-time, and nothing is so changed by distance as the realities of youth. She believed herself to have been actuated by the same calm reason in marrying young John Britton, who had had fair prospects, which she thought should actuate her daughter in marrying Jonathan Nye.

Louisa got no sympathy from her, but she persisted in her refusal. She worked harder and harder. She did not spare herself in doors or out. As the summer wore on her face grew as sunburnt as a boy's, her hands were hard and brown. When she put on her white dress to go to meeting on a Sunday there was a white ring around her neck where the sun had not touched it. Above it her face and neck showed browner. Her sleeves were rather short, and there were also white rings above her brown wrists.

"You look as if you were turnin' Injun by inches," said her mother.

Louisa, when she sat in the meeting-house, tried slyly to pull her sleeves down to the brown on her wrists; she gave a little twitch to the ruffle around her neck. Then she glanced across, and Jonathan Nye was looking at her. She thrust her hands, in their short-wristed, loose cotton gloves, as far out of the sleeves as she could; her brown wrists showed conspicuously on her white lap. She had never heard of the princess who destroyed her beauty that she might not be forced to wed the man whom she did not love, but she had something of the same feeling, although she did not have it for the sake of any tangible lover. Louisa had never seen anybody whom she would have preferred to Jonathan Nye. There was no other marriageable young man in the place. She had only her dreams, which she had in common with other girls.

That Sunday evening before she went to meeting her mother took some old wide lace out of her bureau drawer. "There," said she, "I'm goin' to sew this in your neck an' sleeves before you put your dress on. It'll cover up a little; it's wider than the ruffle."

"I don't want it in," said Louisa.

"I'd like to know why not? You look like a fright. I was ashamed of you this mornin'."

Louisa thrust her arms into the white dress sleeves peremptorily. Her mother did not speak to her all the way to meeting. After meeting, Jonathan Nye walked home with them, and Louisa kept on the other side of her mother. He went into the house and stayed an hour. Mrs Britton entertained him, while Louisa sat silent. When he had gone, she looked at her daughter as if she could have used bodily force, but she said nothing. She shot the bolt of the kitchen door noisily. Louisa lighted her candle. The old man's loud breathing sounded from his room; he had been put to bed for safety before they went to meeting; through the open windows sounded the loud murmur of the summer night, as if that, too, slept heavily.

"Good-night, mother," said Louisa, as she went up-stairs; but her mother did not answer.

The next day was very warm. This was an exceptionally hot summer. Louisa went out early; her mother would not ask her where she was going. She did not come home until noon. Her face was burning; her wet dress clung to her arms and shoulders.

"Where have you been?" asked her mother.

"Oh, I've been out in the field."

"What field?"

"Mr Mitchell's."

"What have you been doin' out there?"

"Rakin' hay."

"Rakin' hay with the men?"

"There wasn't anybody but Mr Mitchell and Johnny. Don't, mother!"

Mrs Britton had turned white. She sank into a chair. "I can't stan' it nohow," she moaned. "All the daughter I've got."

"Don't, mother! I ain't done any harm. What harm is it? Why can't I rake hay as well as a man? Lots of women do such things, if nobody round here does. He's goin' to pay me right off, and we need the money. Don't, mother!" Louisa got a tumbler of water. "Here, mother, drink this."

Mrs Britton pushed it away, Louisa stood looking anxiously at her. Lately her mother had grown thinner than ever; she looked scarcely bigger than a child. Presently she got up and went to the stove.

"Don't try to do anything, mother; let me finish getting dinner," pleaded Louisa. She tried to take the pan of biscuits out of her mother's hands, but she jerked it away.

The old man was sitting on the door-step, huddled up loosely in the sun, like an old dog.

"Come, father," Mrs Britton called, in a dry voice, "dinner's ready – what there is of it!"

The old man shuffled in, smiling.

There was nothing for dinner but the hot biscuits and tea. The fare was daily becoming more meagre. All Louisa's little hoard of school money was gone, and her earnings were very uncertain and slender. Their chief dependence for food through the summer was their garden, but that had failed them in some respects.

One day the old man had come in radiant, with his shaking hands full of potato blossoms; his old eyes twinkled over them like a mischievous child's. Reproaches were useless; the little potato crop was sadly damaged. Lately, in spite of close watching, he had picked the squash blossoms, piling them in a yellow mass beside the kitchen door. Still, it was nearly time for the peas and beans and beets; they would keep them from starvation while they lasted.

But when they came, and Louisa could pick plenty of green food every morning, there was still a difficulty: Mrs Britton's appetite and digestion were poor; she could not live upon a green-vegetable diet; and the old man missed his porridge, for the meal was all gone.

One morning in August he cried at the breakfast-table like a baby, because he wanted his porridge, and Mrs Britton pushed away her own plate with a despairing gesture.

"There ain't no use," said she. "I can't eat no more garden-sauce nohow. I don't blame poor father a mite. You ain't got no feelin' at all."

"I don't know what I can do; I've worked as hard as I can," said Louisa, miserably.

"I know what you can do, and so do you."

"No, I don't, mother," returned Louisa, with alacrity. "He ain't been here for two weeks now, and I saw him with my own eyes yesterday carryin' a dish into the Moselys', and I knew 'twas honey. I think he's after Ida."

"Carryin' honey into the Moselys'? I don't believe it."

"He was; I saw him."

"Well, I don't care if he was. If you're a mind to act decent now, you can bring him round again. He was dead set on you, an' I don't believe he's changed round to that Mosely girl as quick as this."

"You don't want me to ask him to come back here, do you?"

"I want you to act decent. You can go to meetin' to-night, if you're a mind to – I shan't go; I ain't got strength 'nough – an' 'twouldn't hurt you none to hang back a little after meetin', and kind of edge round his way. 'Twouldn't take more'n a look."

"Mother!"

"Well, I don't care. 'Twouldn't hurt you none. It's the way more'n one girl does, whether you believe it or not. Men don't do all the courtin' – not by a long shot. 'Twon't hurt you none. You needn't look so scart."

Mrs Britton's own face was a burning red. She looked angrily away from her daughter's honest, indignant eyes.

"I wouldn't do such a thing as that for a man I liked," said Louisa; "and I certainly shan't for a man I don't like."

"Then me an' your grandfather'll starve," said her mother; "that's all there is about it. We can't neither of us stan' it much longer."

"We could –"

"Could what?"

"Put a – little mortgage on the house."

Mrs Britton faced her daughter. She trembled in every inch of her weak frame. "Put a mortgage on this house, an' by-an'-by not have a roof to cover us! Are you crazy? I tell you what 'tis, Louisa Britton, we may starve, your grandfather an' me, an' you can follow us to the graveyard over there, but there's only one way I'll ever put a mortgage on this house. If you have Jonathan Nye. I'll ask him to take a little one to tide us along an' get your weddin' things."

"Mother, I'll tell you what I'm goin' to do."

"What?"

"I am goin' to ask Uncle Solomon."

"I guess when Solomon Mears does anythin' for us you'll know it. He never forgave your father about that wood lot, an' he's hated the whole of us ever since. When I went to his wife's funeral he never answered when I spoke to him. I guess if you go to him you'll take it out in goin'."

Louisa said nothing more. She began clearing away the breakfast dishes and setting the house to rights. Her mother was actually so weak that she could scarcely stand, and she recognized it. She had settled into the rocking-chair, and leaned her head back. Her face looked pale and sharp against the dark calico cover.

When the house was in order, Louisa stole up-stairs to her own chamber. She put on her clean old blue muslin and her hat, then she went slyly down and out the front way.

It was seven miles to her uncle Solomon Mears's, and she had made up her mind to walk them. She walked quite swiftly until the house windows were out of sight, then she slackened her pace a little. It was one of the fiercest dog-days. A damp heat settled heavily down upon the earth; the sun scalded.

At the foot of the hill Louisa passed a house where one of her girl acquaintances lived. She was going in the gate with a pan of early apples. "Hullo, Louisa," she called.

"Hullo, Vinnie."

"Where you goin'?"

"Oh, I'm goin' a little way."

"Ain't it awful hot? Say, Louisa, do you know Ida Mosely's cuttin' you out?"

"She's welcome."

The other girl, who was larger and stouter than Louisa, with a sallow, unhealthy face, looked at her curiously. "I don't see why you wouldn't have him," said she. "I should have thought you'd jumped at the chance."

"Should you if you didn't like him, I'd like to know?"

"I'd like him if he had such a nice house and as much money as Jonathan Nye," returned the other girl.

She offered Louisa some apples, and she went along the road eating them. She herself had scarcely tasted food that day.

It was about nine o'clock; she had risen early. She calculated how many hours it would take her to walk the seven miles. She walked as fast as she could to hold out. The heat seemed to increase as the sun stood higher. She had walked about three miles when she heard wheels behind her. Presently a team stopped at her side.

"Good-mornin'," said an embarrassed voice.

She looked around. It was Jonathan Nye, with his gray horse and light wagon.

"Good-mornin'," said she.

"Goin' far?"

"A little ways."

"Won't you – ride?"

"No, thank you. I guess I'd rather walk." Jonathan Nye nodded, made an inarticulate noise in his throat, and drove on. Louisa watched the wagon bowling lightly along. The dust flew back. She took out her handkerchief and wiped her dripping face.

It was about noon when she came in sight of her uncle Solomon Mears's house in Wolfsborough. It stood far back from the road, behind a green expanse of untrodden yard. The blinds on the great square front were all closed; it looked as if everybody were away. Louisa went around to the side door. It stood wide open. There was a thin blue cloud of tobacco smoke issuing from it. Solomon Mears sat there in the large old kitchen smoking his pipe. On the table near him was an empty bowl; he had just eaten his dinner of bread and milk. He got his own dinner, for he had lived alone since his wife died. He looked at Louisa. Evidently he did not recognize her.

"How do you do, Uncle Solomon?" said Louisa.

"Oh, it's John Britton's daughter! How d'ye do?" He took his pipe out of his mouth long enough to speak, then replaced it. His eyes, sharp under their shaggy brows, were fixed on Louisa; his broad bristling face had a look of stolid rebuff like an ox; his stout figure, in his soiled farmer dress, surged over his chair. He sat full in the doorway. Louisa standing before him, the perspiration trickling over her burning face, set forth her case with a certain dignity. This old man was her mother's nearest relative. He had property and to spare. Should she survive him, it would be hers, unless willed away. She, with her unsophisticated sense of justice, had a feeling that he ought to help her.

The old man listened. When she stopped speaking he took the pipe out of his mouth slowly, and stared gloomily past her at his hay field, where the grass was now a green stubble.

"I ain't got no money I can spare jest now," said he. "I s'pose you know your father cheated me out of consider'ble once?"

"We don't care so much about money, if you have got something you could spare to – eat. We ain't got anything but garden-stuff."

Solomon Mears still frowned past her at the hay field. Presently he arose slowly and went across the kitchen. Louisa sat down on the door-step and waited. Her uncle was gone quite a while. She, too, stared over at the field, which seemed to undulate like a lake in the hot light.

"Here's some things you can take, if you want 'em" said her uncle, at her back.

She got up quickly. He pointed grimly to the kitchen table. He was a deacon, an orthodox believer; he recognized the claims of the poor, but he gave alms as a soldier might yield up his sword. Benevolence was the result of warfare with his own conscience.

On the table lay a ham, a bag of meal, one of flour, and a basket of eggs.

"I'm afraid I can't carry 'em all," said Louisa.

"Leave what you can't then." Solomon caught up his hat and went out. He muttered something about not spending any more time as he went.

Louisa stood looking at the packages. It was utterly impossible for her to carry them all at once. She heard her uncle shout to some oxen he was turning out of the barn. She took up the bag of meal and the basket of eggs and carried them out to the gate; then she returned, got the flour and ham, and went with them to a point beyond. Then she returned for the meal and eggs, and carried them past the others. In that way she traversed the seven miles home. The heat increased. She had eaten nothing since morning but the apples that her friend had given her. Her head was swimming, but she kept on. Her resolution was as immovable under the power of the sun as a rock. Once in a while she rested for a moment under a tree, but she soon arose and went on. It was like a pilgrimage, and the Mecca at the end of the burning, desert-like road was her own maiden independence.

It was after eight o'clock when she reached home. Her mother stood in the doorway watching for her, straining her eyes in the dusk.

"For goodess sake, Louisa Britton! where have you been?" she began; but Louisa laid the meal and eggs down on the step.

"I've got to go back a little ways," she panted.

When she returned with the flour and ham, she could hardly get into the house. She laid them on the kitchen table, where her mother had put the other parcels, and sank into a chair.

"Is this the way you've brought all these things home?" asked her mother.

Louisa nodded.

"All the way from Uncle Solomon's?"

"Yes."

Her mother went to her and took her hat off. "It's a mercy if you ain't got a sunstroke," said she, with a sharp tenderness. "I've got somethin' to tell you. What do you s'pose has happened? Mr Mosely has been here, an' he wants you to take the school again when it opens next week. He says Ida ain't very well, but I guess that ain't it. They think she's goin' to get somebody. Mis' Mitchell says so. She's been in. She says he's carryin' things over there the whole time, but she don't believe there's anything settled yet. She says they feel so sure of it they're goin' to have Ida give the school up. I told her I thought Ida would make him a good wife, an' she was easier suited than some girls. What do you s'pose Mis' Mitchell says? She says old Mis' Nye told her that there was one thing about it: if Jonathan had you, he wa'n't goin' to have me an' father hitched on to him; he'd look out for that. I told Mis' Mitchell that I guess there wa'n't none of us willin' to hitch, you nor anybody else. I hope she'll tell Mis' Nye. Now I'm a-goin' to turn you out a tumbler of milk – Mis' Mitchell she brought over a whole pitcherful; says she's got more'n they can use – they ain't got no pig now – an' then you go an' lay down on the sittin'-room lounge, an' cool off; an' I'll stir up some porridge for supper, an' boil some eggs. Father'll be tickled to death. Go right in there. I'm dreadful afraid you'll be sick. I never heard of anybody doin' such a thing as you have.''

Louisa drank the milk and crept into the sitting-room. It was warm and close there, so she opened the front door and sat down on the step. The twilight was deep, but there was a clear yellow glow in the west. One great star had come out in the midst of it. A dewy coolness was spreading over everything. The air was full of bird calls and children's voices. Now and then there was a shout of laughter. Louisa leaned her head against the door-post.

The house was quite near the road. Someone passed – a man carrying a basket. Louisa glanced at him, and recognized Jonathan Nye by his gait. He kept on down the road towards the Moseleys', and Louisa turned again from him to her sweet, mysterious, girlish dreams.

Kate Chopin

Désirée's Baby

As the day was pleasant, Madame Valmondé drove over to L'Abri to see Désirée and the baby.

It made her laugh to think of Désirée with a baby. Why, it seemed but yesterday that Désirée was little more than a baby herself; when Monsieur in riding through the gateway of Valmondé had found her lying asleep in the shadow of the big stone pillar.

The little one awoke in his arms and began to cry for "Dada." That was as much as she could do or say. Some people thought she might have strayed there of her own accord, for she was of the toddling age. The prevailing belief was that she had been purposely left by a party of Texans, whose canvas-covered wagon, late in the day, had crossed the ferry that Coton Mais kept, just below the plantation. In time Madame Valmondé abandoned every speculation but the one that Désirée had been sent to her by a beneficent Providence to be the child of her affection, seeing that she was without child of the flesh. For the girl grew to be beautiful and gentle, affectionate and sincere, – the idol of Valmondé.

It was no wonder, when she stood one day against the stone pillar in whose shadow she had lain asleep, eighteen years before, that Armand Aubigny riding by and seeing her there, had fallen in love with her. That was the way all the Aubignys fell in love, as if struck by a pistol shot. The wonder was that he had not loved her before; for he had known her since his father brought him home from Paris, a boy of eight, after his mother died there. The passion that awoke in him that day, when he saw her at the gate, swept along like an avalanche, or like a prairie fire, or like anything that drives headlong over all obstacles.

Monsieur Valmondé grew practical and wanted things well considered: that is, the girl's obscure origin. Armand looked into her eyes and did not care. He was reminded that she was nameless. What did it matter about a name when he could give her one of the oldest and proudest in Louisiana? He ordered the *corbeille* from Paris, and contained himself with what patience he could until it arrived; then they were married.

Madame Valmondé had not seen Désirée and the baby for four weeks. When she reached L'Abri she shuddered at the first sight of it, as she always did. It was a sad looking place, which for many years had not known the gentle presence of a mistress, old Monsieur Aubigny having married and buried his wife in France, and she having loved her own land too well ever to leave it. The roof came down steep black like a cowl, reaching out beyond the wide galleries that encircled the yellow stuccoed house. Big, solemn oaks grew close to it, and their thick-leaved, farreaching branches shadowed it like a pall. Young Aubigny's rule was a strict one, too, and under it his negroes had forgotten how to be gay, as they had been during the old master's easygoing and indulgent lifetime.

The young mother was recovering slowly, and lay full length, in her soft white muslins and laces, upon a couch. The baby was beside her, upon her arm, where he had fallen asleep, at her breast. The yellow nurse woman sat beside a window fanning herself.

Madame Valmondé bent her portly figure over Désirée and kissed her, holding her an instant tenderly in her arms. Then she turned to the child.

"This is not the baby!" she exclaimed, in startled tones. French was the language spoken at Valmondé in those days.

"I knew you would be astonished," laughed Désirée, "at the way he has grown. The little *cochon de lait!* Look at his legs, mamma, and his hands and fingernails – real finger-nails. Zandrine had to cut them this morning. Isn't it true, Zandrine?"

The woman bowed her turbaned head majestically, "Mais si, Madame."

"And the way he cries," went on Désirée, "is deafening. Armand heard him the other day as far away as La Blanche's cabin."

Madame Valmondé had never removed her eyes from the child. She lifted it and walked with it over to the window that was lightest. She scanned the baby narrowly, then looked as searchingly at Zandrine, whose face was turned to gaze across the fields.

"Yes, the child has grown, has changed," said Madame Valmondé, slowly, as she replaced it beside its mother. "What does Armand say?"

Désirée's face became suffused with a glow that was happiness itself.

"Oh, Armand is the proudest father in the parish, I believe, chiefly because it is a boy, to bear his name; though he says not, – that he would have loved a girl as well. But I know it isn't true. I know he says that to please me. And mamma," she added, drawing Madame Valmondé's head down to her, and speaking in a whisper, "he hasn't punished one of them – not one of them since baby is born. Even Négrillon, who pretended to have burnt his leg that he might rest from work – he only laughed, and said Négrillon was a great scamp. Oh, mamma, I'm so happy; it frightens me."

What Désirée said was true. Marriage, and later the birth of his son had softened Armand Aubigny's imperious and exacting nature greatly. This was what made the gentle Désirée so happy, for she loved him desperately. When he frowned she trembled, but loved him. When he smiled, she asked no greater blessing of God. But Armand's dark, handsome face had not often been disfigured by frowns since the day he fell in love with her.

When the baby was about three months old, Désirée awoke one day to the conviction that there was something in the air menacing her peace. It was at first too subtle to grasp. It had only been a disquieting suggestion; an air of mystery among the blacks; unexpected visits from far-off neighbors who could hardly account for their coming. Then a strange, an awful change in her husband's manner, which she dared not ask him to explain. When he spoke to her, it was with averted eyes, from which the old love-light seemed to have gone out. He absented himself from home; and when there, avoided her presence and that of her child, without excuse. And the very spirit of Satan seemed suddenly to take hold of him in his dealings with the slaves. Désirée was miserable enough to die.

She sat in her room, one hot afternoon, in her *peignoir*, listlessly drawing through her fingers the strands of her long, silky brown hair that hung about her shoulders. The baby, half naked, lay asleep upon her own great mahogany bed, that was like a sumptuous throne, with its satin-lined half-canopy. One of La Blanche's little quadroon boys – half naked too – stood fanning the child slowly with a fan of peacock feathers. Désirée's eyes had been fixed absently and sadly upon the baby, while she was striving to penetrate the threatening mist that she felt closing about her. She looked from her child to the boy who stood beside him, and back again; over and over. "Ah!" It was a cry that she could not help; which she was not conscious of having uttered. The blood turned like ice in her veins, and a clammy moisture gathered upon her face.

She tried to speak to the little quadroon boy; but no sound would come, at first. When he heard his name uttered, he looked up, and his mistress was pointing to the door. He laid aside the great, soft fan, and obediently stole away, over the polished floor, on his bare tiptoes.

She stayed motionless, with gaze riveted upon her child, and her face the picture of fright.

Presently her husband entered the room, and without noticing her, went to a table and began to search among some papers which covered it.

"Armand," she called to him, in a voice which must have stabbed him, if he was human. But he did not notice. "Armand," she said again. Then she rose and tottered towards him. "Armand," she panted once more, clutching his arm, "look at our child. What does it mean? Tell me."

He coldly but gently loosened her fingers from about his arm and thrust the hand away from him. "Tell me what it means!" she cried despairingly.

"It means," he answered lightly, "that the child is not white; it means that you are not white."

A quick conception of all that this accusation meant for her nerved her with unwonted courage to deny it. "It is a lie; it is not true, I am white! Look at my hair, it is brown; and my eyes are gray, Armand, you know they are gray. And my skin is fair," seizing his wrist. "Look at my hand; whiter than yours, Armand," she laughed hysterically.

"As white as La Blanche's," he returned cruelly; and went away leaving her alone with their child.

When she could hold a pen in her hand, she sent a despairing letter to Madame Valmondé.

"My mother, they tell me I am not white. Armand has told me I am not white. For God's sake tell them it is not true. You must know it is not true. I shall die. I must die. I cannot be so unhappy, and live."

The answer that came was as brief:

"My own Désirée: Come home to Valmondé; back to your mother who loves you. Come with your child."

When the letter reached Désirée she went with it to her husband's study, and laid it open upon the desk before which he sat. She was like a stone image: silent, white, motionless after she placed it there.

In silence he ran his cold eyes over the written words. He said nothing. "Shall I go, Armand?" she asked in tones sharp with agonized suspense.

"Yes, go."

"Do you want me to go?"

"Yes, I want you to go."

He thought Almighty God had dealt cruelly and unjustly with him; and felt, somehow, that he was paying Him back in kind when he stabbed thus into his wife's soul. Moreover he no longer loved her, because of the unconscious injury she had brought upon his home and his name.

She turned away like one stunned by a blow, and walked slowly towards the door, hoping he would call her back.

"Good-bye, Armand," she moaned.

He did not answer her. That was his last blow at fate.

Désirée went in search of her child. Zandrine was pacing the sombre gallery with it. She took the little one from the nurse's arms with no word of explanation, and descending the steps, walked away, under the live-oak branches.

It was an October afternoon; the sun was just sinking. Out in the still fields the negroes were picking cotton.

Désirée had not changed the thin white garment nor the slippers which she wore. Her hair was uncovered and the sun's rays brought a golden gleam from its brown meshes. She did not take the broad, beaten road which led to the far-off plantation of Valmondé. She walked across a deserted field, where the stubble bruised her tender feet, so delicately shod, and tore her thin gown to shreds.

She disappeared among the reeds and willows that grew thick along the banks of the deep, sluggish bayou; and she did not come back again.

Some weeks later there was a curious scene enacted at L'Abri. In the centre of the smoothly swept back yard was a great bonfire. Armand Aubigny sat in the wide hallway that commanded a view of the spectacle; and it was he who dealt out to a half dozen negroes the material which kept this fire ablaze.

A graceful cradle of willow, with all its dainty furbishings, was laid upon the pyre, which had already been fed with the richness of a priceless *layette*. Then there were silk gowns, and velvet and satin ones added to these; laces, too, and embroideries; bonnets and gloves; for the *corbeille* had been of rare quality.

The last thing to go was a tiny bundle of letters; innocent little scribblings that Désirée had sent to him during the days of their espousal. There was the remnant of one back in the drawer from which he took them. But it was not Désirée; it was part of an old letter from his mother to his father. He read it. She was thanking God for the blessing of her husband's love:—

"But, above all," she wrote, "night and day, I thank the good God for having so arranged our lives that our dear Armand will never know that his mother, who adores him, belongs to the race that is cursed with the brand of slavery."

Doris Lessing

A Proper Marriage

"Lie down," said the nurse, sharp with impatience.

Martha climbed with difficulty on to one of the high narrow beds, and almost at once Dr. Stern came in.

"Well, Mrs. Knowell? You girls all insist on having your babies in the small hours." She knew him well enough by now to understand that he had said this many times before. Once again she submitted to those skilled impersonal hands, while he remarked that it was a good time of the year for having babies, she had done well to arrange things thus. He then removed his hands, said, "Fine, fine," and turned to depart. Martha, who had half believed that this was nearly over, demanded how long it would be; at which he remarked absorbedly, on his way out, that she must be a good girl, and be patient. The door swung silently shut behind him, and she was alone.

For some time she lay stiff on the very narrow slope of the bed, and waited. In this position, it seemed that the pains were worse. Or rather that she could not command herself as well. She climbed down, and walked up and down the deserted room. Now it was every four minutes, and she was doubled up with them, shutting her teeth against the desire to groan, cautiously unfolding herself again. She noticed she was wet with sweat. It was very hot in the room. She went to the window and looked out. Across the faintly moonlit veld, the glow from the city burned steadily, swallowing a glitter of stars. The stars vanished in another hot wave of pain. This time she found herself crouching on the floor, astonished and indignant at the violence of it. The pain had swallowed *her* up; and dismay at having lost guard caused her to return to the bed, where she might keep her attention on the process, keep that sentinel alert against the dark engulfing sea. Tight, stiff, cautious, she felt the baby knot and propel itself down; it recoiled and slackened, and she with it. The pain had changed. She could mark the point at which, just as it had abruptly changed its quality a couple of hours before in the bath, so now it ground into a new gear, as it were. It gripped first her back, then her stomach, then it was as if she and the baby were being wrung out together by a pair of enormous steel hands. But still she kept that small place in her brain alive and watchful. She would *not* give in. She lay like a tight spring, with half her attention given to not rolling off the bed, or table – which was so narrow she could not have turned on it – and concentrated.

The baby-faced nurse hurried in, and inquired, "How are you doing?" And hurried out again. Martha, engulfed in a pain, most passionately resented that uncommitted virgin with her determination not to be disturbed by suffering. But it was to the practical cool little voice that she was submitted; and when, at some indeterminate time later, the nurse came back, to say that Martha was being a good girl, and in the morning she would have a comfortable bed, she was able to achieve a humorous gasp that she wouldn't mind a comfortable bed now.

"Well, what can we do?" demanded the pink girl. "We can't help it if all the babies decided to get born at once, can we?" She vanished again, remarking, "We've got three of them out, that's something. Let's pray no more of you come in tonight."

Martha no longer had the energy to achieve a mild amusement. The small lit place in her brain was dimming most alarmingly with the pains. Every time, the light nearly went out; always, it flickered precariously and shone up again. Martha noted that something new was happening to time. The watch that lay six inches from her nose on her crooked arm said the pains were punctual at two minutes. But from the moment that the warning hot wave of pain swept up her back, she entered a place where there was no time at all. An agony so unbelievable gripped her that her astounded and protesting mind cried out it was impossible such pain should be. It was a pain so violent that it was no longer pain, but a condition of being. Every particle of flesh shrieked out, while the wave spurted like an electric current from somewhere in her backbone and went through her in shock after shock. The wave receded, however, just as she had decided she would disintegrate under it; and then she felt the fist that gripped her slowly loosen. Through the sweat in her eyes she saw that ten seconds had passed; she went limp, into a state of perfect painlessness, an exquisite exhaustion in which the mere idea of pain seemed impossible – it was impossible that it could recur again. And as soon as the

123

slow flush of sensation began, the condition of painlessness seemed as impossible as the pain had seemed only a few moments before. They were two states of being, utterly disconnected, without a bridge, and Martha found herself in a condition of anxious but exasperated anger that she could *not* remember the agony fifteen seconds after it had ended. She was now lying almost naked, her great tight knotted belly sticking up in a purple lump, watching with fascination how it contracted and strained, while she kept alert the determination not to lose control of the process; while she was lit with curiosity as to the strange vagaries of time and, above all, and increasingly, almost to the point of weeping fury, that all her concentration, all her self-consciousness, could not succeed in creating the state of either pain or painlessness while its opposite was in her. It was a complete failure of her, the free spirit: how was it possible not to remember something that had passed ten seconds before, and would recur so soon? The anger at her failure was strong enough nearly, but not quite, to quench that part of her mind which must stay alert. She sobered herself. When the wave of pain had receded, and she lay spent, she was grimly flogging her mind to *imagine* the quality of the pain that had just gone. Impossible. And when she was writhing in the grip of the giant fist, she was gasping with determination to *imagine* no pain. She could not. With all her determination, she could not. There were two Marthas, and there was nothing to bridge them. Failure. Complete failure. She was helpless with rage. She heard the pain-gripped Martha cry out, "Oh, God, oh God!" and she was curious at the ancient being in her that cried out to God. Damned liar, coward, idiot! said Martha to herself from across the gulf. It only needs that you should call out "Mother!" And behold, Martha, that free spirit, understood from the exquisite shore of complete, empty non-sensation that she had been groaning out "Mother, Mother, Mother!" Without a flicker of feeling in any part of her body, she felt the tears of failure roll down her face; and looked up through them to see the pink nurse looking down at her with unmistakable disappointment.

"Well, dear," said the girl disapprovingly, "it's no good carrying on like that *yet*." Her plump little hands, tightly sealed in pink rubber, went plunging into Martha's body. "Not nearly yet, you know," she remarked, regarding Martha while she grunted and rolled in another pain. "And anyway," heard

Martha, the young bright voice coming distorted through hot agony, "we've got to get this other baby born before we can attend to you. Do you think you could hold it a bit?"

Martha saw the door open, and a stretcher wheeled in. Suddenly the room was filled with people. She saw a woman, similarly grotesque, inhuman, grunting, being rolled over on to the other narrow high table, while Dr. Stern and a couple of nurses stood about with a look of intent concentration. Then the white screens went up and hid them. Martha looked away, and submitted to another trial. The woman on the other table seemed to be having pains about every half minute; what Martha's determination could not achieve, her nerves could: she suffered in her flesh that other woman's pains, like a counterpoint, a faint but faithful echo of her own, in jarring opposite to her own rhythm. Suddenly the sounds of striving flesh ceased, a faint smell of chloroform was in the air; Martha found herself avidly breathing it in. Instruments clinked; she heard Dr. Stern's voice giving orders; she heard the stiff rustle of starch. There was a gasp, and a baby started crying.

"For God's sake," nagged Martha to her child, "get yourself out of there quickly." The child, however, was crouched waiting for the next spring forward; and Martha watched the flesh shrink and harden in the new contraction. This time she heard herself give a shriek. She no longer cared at all. All she fought for was to drag herself as soon as possible out of each gulf, not to give in more than she had to.

A long time passed; she rolled her eyes to the window and saw that it showed grey light; a single white star hung quivering; it faded; a pink flush crept up the sky. She heard the sound of a wet brush on a floor. It was a native woman, on her knees with a scrubbing brush. The screens had gone from the other white bed. Martha tensed and groaned, and the native woman raised her head, looked over, and smiled encouragement. There was no one else in the room. Martha could hear the cacophony of screaming babies from the other end of the building.

The native woman gave a quick look into the passage, and then came over to Martha. She was young, her dark face polished and smiling. She wore a neat white cloth on her head. She laid her wet dirty hand on Martha's striving stomach. "Bad," she said, in her rich voice. "Bad. Bad." As a fresh pain came, she said, "Let the baby come, let the baby come, let the baby come." It was a croon, an old nurse's song. Martha trembled with exhaustion, and tensed herself, but the woman smiled down and sang, "Yes, missus, yes, let it come, let it come."

Martha let the cold knot of determination loosen, she let herself go, she let her mind go dark into the pain.

"That's right, missus, that's right, that's right."

Suddenly the hand was withdrawn, leaving a cold wetness on her stomach. Martha looked, and saw that the native woman was on her knees with the scrubbing brush, and the young pink nurse stood beside her, looking suspiciously at the scrubbing woman. The brush was going slosh, slosh, wetly and regularly over the floor. Martha listened to the sound as if it were the pulse of her own nature, and did not listen as the pink nurse lifted her legs, levered them energetically up and down, and said, "That's the stuff, push!" Later, Martha heard the bright voice calling from the door, "Yes, doctor, she's ripe!" The room was full of people again. She was sucking in chloroform like an addict, and no longer even remembered that she had been determined to see the child born.

When her eyes cleared, she caught a glimpse of Dr. Stern holding up a naked pallid infant, its dark hair plastered wet in streaks to its head, mouthing frustratedly at the air. Martha momentarily lost consciousness again, and emerged, feeling it must be years later, to see Dr. Stern, in the same position, still holding the white baby, which looked rather like a forked parsnip and was making strangled, grumbling gasps. Two nurses were watching him. They looked triumphant and pleased. This humanity comforted Martha. She heard one say, "A lovely little girl, isn't she?" Then the pink nurse bent over her and began lifting handfuls of Martha's now slack stomach, and squeezing it like oranges. Martha shrieked, with the intention of being heard. "Oh, drat it," said the nurse; and the dome of white chloroform came down again over Martha's face.

This time her eyes opened on a scene of white beds, and faces leaning against white pillows. After a time, she realized that she was pillowed at last in comfort. Five women were in the other beds. Excitement flooded her, and she attempted to sit up. The lower part of her body announced that it was bruised and sore, and did not want to move. Martha raised herself on her hands and the women next to her asked how she felt. Martha was struck by the lazy self-absorption of that voice. She said she felt fine, and the woman nodded. But her eyes were on the door. It opened, and the pink nurse entered with five babies balanced all over her arms. They were yelling, with hungry open mouths. The babies were plopped neatly one after another on to the beds, and gathered in by the waiting mothers. The pink nurse, empty-armed, arrived at Martha's bed, and enquired, "Well, how are you?"

"Where's my baby?" asked Martha anxiously.

"She's having a nice rest," said the nurse, already on her way out.

"But I haven't seen her yet," said Martha, weak tears behind her lids.

"You don't want to disturb her, do you?" said the nurse disapprovingly.

The door shut. The woman, whose long full breast sloped already into the baby's mouth, looked up and said, "You'd better do as they want, dear. It saves trouble. They've got their own ideas."

Martha, cheated and empty, lay and watched the other women suckle their babies. It was intolerable that after nine months of close companionship with the creature, now announced as a girl, she might not even make its acquaintance. There was something impossible in the idea that yesterday the child had been folded in her flesh and it now lay rooms away, washed and clothed, in a cradle with its name on it. It made her uneasy; she wanted to see it – she even felt irrationally that the child might have died at birth and they were lying to her.

Then she remembered the moment when she had seen it lifted, mouthing and struggling for air, and winced suddenly with remembered pain. She had entered on a new state. The shadow of the pain she had felt, though not the terrible intensity of it, threatened her. She must not think of it, as otherwise the bruised flesh of her stomach began to contract in remembered waves of pain. Also, the absolute peace of those moments between the pains had gone. She was sore and aching, and her body was gripped tight in a stiff roll of stuff, under which she could feel the slack flesh folded together.

The babies lapsed into content all round her, and she watched them being taken away. The elation she felt, the achievement, slackened into disappointment.

When Douglas came in that afternoon, beaming, rubbing his hands with pride, smelling strongly of beer, her intention to appeal to him vanished in dislike. He announced with pride that he and Willie had been giving it a bang with the boys all night, he had not been to bed, he had rung up the home at half-hour intervals until Miss Galbind had told him he was a nuisance. He said, too, that the baby·was fine.

"I haven't seen her," said Martha faintly.

"Oh, well, they know best," he said.

At this moment Mrs. Quest entered, tremulous with emotion, and said that the baby was beautiful, but that she was quite sure the nurses had no idea how to treat a new baby; she had a good idea to go to the matron. At this Martha reacted with the announcement that the nursing-home people certainly knew what they were doing.

When Douglas and Mrs. Quest left, Martha lay and quivered with anger and frustration. It was late afternoon. For the third time she saw the white bundles brought in and handed to the mothers, while she lay watching.

Late that evening, after the babies had been fed for the last time, Miss Galbind briskly entered and asked if everyone was happy, and Martha enquired when she could see her baby.

"You want to see her, do you?" enquired Miss Galbind reasonably. "Oh, well, I suppose you may as well." She departed, having shed friendly good nights around the room; and Martha raised herself, waiting for the moment.

But it seemed Miss Galbind was in no hurry; half an hour crawled by, while Martha watched the door. At last the pink nurse entered, with a tight white bundle, and deposited it carelessly on the bed. "There's your daughter," she announced. "Five minutes, now."

Under the jealous inspection of the pink nurse, Martha turned back the flap of blanket, and saw a tiny flushed sleeping face. Again curiosity flooded over into a passionate protective tenderness, and she held the baby close; but the nurse, restlessly hovering at the side of the bed, decided it was enough.

"Now then," she announced, "you'll have enough of her in the next few months, I bet!" And with this she deftly removed the bundle, and went out with it, switching off the lights.

The other five women had already laid themselves down for the night. Martha, who to her fury once again discovered that she wanted only to cry, looked around for support. She caught the eye of the woman in the next bed, who said kindly, "It's no good getting upset. They'll let you have her in the morning, I expect." She turned herself carefully on to her side, and shut her eyes, in an obvious determination to submit to the routine and get it over. She remarked, with closed eyes, "This is my third, I always say I'll never come here again, but it's easier on the whole. You can do what you like when you get home, that's a comfort." She began breathing deeply.

Martha lay tensely awake. She heard a car drive up: another baby was due to be born; but already the condition of waiting for a baby to be born seemed far behind. She felt a calm superiority over the women who still had to go through with it. But when, later, doors opened and shut, feet hurried, and a woman began moaning down the passage, she had to bury her head in the pillow, because each moan seemed to drag a wave of pain out of her own stomach. She could not sleep. Excitement was beating through her. She was longing for the morning – perhaps then she might be allowed to feed the baby. The women slept heavily all around her, reminding her, with their heavy breathing, of cows on a dark hillside. But her mind was at the other end of the building, in the room full of babies. She watched the stars move across the windows, and wished they might hurry, hurry, hurry to the dawn. Then a baby began crying, a faint persistent wail, and soon they were all crying. The women began stirring and listening in their beds.

The woman in the next bed said in a resigned voice, "Well, they're as tough as anything, that's a comfort." She was lying tense; Martha saw she was crying. This upset her – the mother of three, calmly resigned, had given her strength to bear her own childish impatiences.

"What's the matter?" asked Martha anxiously. Then: "Are the babies hungry?"

The woman gave a weak laugh through her tears, and said, "They can't be hungry till six. It's against the rules." Then she turned herself over with another cautious heave, and remarked, "I always cry like a leaking tap for weeks after I have a baby. Don't take any notice."

For a while Martha saw how the woman turned and tossed, listening; then the chorus of crying dimmed and they slept again. Martha heard the cocks crow, and then again. She could see the Seven Sisters, a faint clustering glow over a spiring black gum tree. The babies began to scream again. It was nearly dawn. The sky was lightening. The women sat up, blinking, as the lights came on and a bright gay voice shouted, "Get ready, girls." It was morning, though the stars were shining outside. It was half past four.

"What's funny is this," said the woman next to Martha, with tolerant good nature, "it's supposed to be six, but even the nurses can't stick it out, so they stretch it a bit."

Half an hour passed. "My breasts are dripping," said one woman. "Every morning my bed's flooded," said another. Martha was helpless with envy. Her breasts were still limp.

This time six small yelling bundles came in on a trolley. Martha received her daughter with trembling eagerness. The baby was crying; it looked, to Martha, distressed, hot and miserable. She took the little thing, and held the yelling round mouth to her nipple. It moved in sudden desperate silence this way and that, eyes showing anxious gleams of blue, and then – miracle! – the lips fastened and began to suck. Strong waves of suction passed through Martha and into her womb with contractions of pain. She did not expect this, and moved uncomfortably, gripping herself against it. The baby sucked steadily, small slits of hazy blue showing in the tiny red face. Martha daringly undid the tight roll, and the infant fell loosely into the shape of a baby, so that Martha was able to hold it to herself comfortably, instead of in the shape of a papoose. She moved it over to the other breast, admonishing both to be quick and supply milk.

Miss Galbind came springing silently in, and stood watchfully over Martha. "All right," she announced, after a minute, "she's a good sucker." With this she removed the child, rolled it again into the papoose of white blanket, and said, "That's enough for a start." She went out, the baby tucked under her arm like a long parcel sticking out behind.

"Don't worry," said the woman in the next bed, giving Martha an amused look. "You can do anything to a baby, even bounce it."

Edna O'Brien

Cords

Everything was ready, the suitcase closed, her black velvet coat-collar carefully brushed, and a list pinned to the wall reminding her husband when to feed the hens and turkeys, and what food-stuffs to give them. She was setting out on a visit to her daughter Claire in London, just like any mother, except that *her* daughter was different: she'd lost her faith, and she mixed with queer people and wrote poems. If it was stories one could detect the sin in them, but these poems made no sense at all and therefore seemed more wicked. Her daughter had sent the money for the air-ticket. She was going now, kissing her husband goodbye, tender towards him in a way that she never was, throughout each day, as he spent his time looking through the window at the wet currant bushes, grumbling about the rain, but was in fact pleased at the excuse to hatch indoors, and asked for tea all the time, which he lapped from a saucer, because it was more pleasurable.

"The turkeys are the most important," she said, kissing him good-bye, and thinking faraway to the following Christmas, to the turkeys she would sell, and the plumper ones she would give as gifts.

"I hope you have a safe flight," he said. She'd never flown before.

"All Irish planes are blessed, they never crash," she said, believing totally in the God that created her, sent her this venial husband, a largish farmhouse, hens, hardship, and one daughter who'd changed, become moody, and grown away from them completely.

The journey was pleasant once she'd got over the shock of being strapped down for the take-off. As they went higher and higher she looked out at the very white, wispish cloud and thought of the wash tub and hoped her husband would remember to change his shirt while she was away. The trip would have been perfect but that there was a screaming woman

132

who had to be calmed down by the air hostess. She looked like a woman who was being sent to a mental institution, but did not know it.

Claire met her mother at the airport and they kissed warmly, not having seen each other for over a year.

"Have you stones in it?" Claire said, taking the fibre suitcase. It was doubly secured with a new piece of binding twine. Her mother wore a black straw hat with clusters of cherries on both sides of the brim.

"You were great to meet me," the mother said.

"Of course I'd meet you," Claire said, easing her mother right back on the taxi seat. It was a long ride and they might as well be comfortable.

"I could have navigated," the mother said, and Claire said nonsense a little too brusquely. Then to make amends she asked gently how the journey was.

"Oh I must tell you, there was this very peculiar woman and she was screaming."

Claire listened and stiffened, remembering her mother's voice that became low and dramatic in a crisis, the same voice that said, "Sweet Lord your father will kill us", or, "What's to become of us, the bailiff is here", or, "Look, look, the chimney is on fire."

"But otherwise?" Claire said. This was a holiday, not an expedition into the past.

"We had tea and sandwiches. I couldn't eat mine, the bread was buttered."

"Still faddy?" Claire said. Her mother got bilious if she touched butter, fish, olive oil, or eggs; although her daily diet was mutton stew, or home-cured bacon.

"Anyhow, I have nice things for you," Claire said. She had bought in stocks of biscuits, jellies and preserves because these were the things her mother favoured, these foods that she herself found distasteful.

The first evening passed well enough. The mother unpacked the presents – a chicken, bread, eggs, a tapestry of a church spire which she'd done all winter, stitching at it until she was almost blind, a holy water font, ashtrays made from shells, lamps converted from bottles, and a picture of a matador assembled by sticking small varnished pebbles on to hardboard.

Claire laid them along the mantleshelf in the kitchen, and

stood back, not so much to admire them as to see how incongruous they looked, piled together.

"Thank you," she said to her mother, as tenderly as she might have when she was a child. These gifts touched her, especially the tapestry, although it was ugly. She thought of the winter nights and the Aladdin lamp smoking (they expected the electricity to be installed soon), and her mother hunched over her work, not even using a thimble to ease the needle through, because she believed in sacrifice, and her father turning to say, "Could I borrow your glasses, Mam, I want to have a look at the paper?" He was too lazy to have his own eyes tested and believed that his wife's glasses were just as good. She could picture them at the fire night after night, the turf flames green and fitful, the hens locked up, foxes prowling around in the wind, outside.

"I'm glad you like it, I did it specially for you," the mother said gravely, and they both stood with tears in their eyes, savouring those seconds of tenderness, knowing that it would be short-lived.

"You'll stay seventeen days," Claire said, because that was the length an economy ticket allowed. She really meant, "Are you staying seventeen days?"

"If it's all right," her mother said over-humbly. "I don't see you that often, and I miss you."

Claire withdrew into the scullery to put on the kettle for her mother's hot water bottle; she did not want any disclosures now, any declaration about how hard life had been and how near they'd been to death during many of the father's drinking deliriums.

"Your father sent you his love," her mother said, nettled because Claire had not asked how he was.

"How is he?"

"He's great now, never touches a drop."

Claire knew that if he had, he would have descended on her, the way he used to descend on her as a child when she was in the convent, or else she would have had a telegram, of clipped urgency, "Come home. Mother."

"It was God did it, curing him like that," the mother said.

Claire thought bitterly that God had taken too long to help the thin frustrated man who was emaciated, crazed and bankrupted by drink. But she said nothing, she merely filled the rubber bottle, pressed the air from it with her arm, and then conducted her mother upstairs to bed.

Next morning they went up to the centre of London and Claire presented her mother with fifty pounds. The woman got flushed and began to shake her head, the quick uncontrolled movements resembling those of a beast with the staggers.

"You always had a good heart, too good," she said to her daughter, as her eyes beheld racks of coats, raincoats, skirts on spinning hangers, and all kinds and colours of hats.

"Try some on," Claire said. "I have to make a phone call."

There were guests due to visit her that night – it had been arranged weeks before – but as they were bohemian people, she could not see her mother suffering them, or them suffering her mother. There was the added complication that they were a 'trio' – one man and two women; his wife and his mistress. At that point in their lives the wife was noticeably pregnant.

On the telephone the mistress said they were looking forward, awfully, to the night, and Claire heard herself substantiate the invitation by saying she had simply rung up to remind them. She thought of asking another man to give a complexion of decency to the evening, but the only three unattached men she could think of had been lovers of hers and she could not call on them; it seemed pathetic.

"Damn," she said, irritated by many things, but mainly by the fact that she was going through one of those bleak, loveless patches that come in everyone's life, but, she imagined, came more frequently the older one got. She was twenty-eight. Soon she would be thirty. Withering.

"How do?" her mother said in a ridiculous voice when Claire returned. She was holding a hand mirror up to get a back view of a ridiculous hat, which she had tried on. It resembled the shiny straw she wore for her trip, except that it was more ornamental and cost ten guineas. That was the second point about it that Claire noted. The white price tag was hanging over the mother's nose. Claire hated shopping the way other people might hate going to the dentist. For herself she never shopped. She merely saw things in windows, ascertained the size, and bought them.

"Am I too old for it?" the mother said. A loaded question in itself.

"You're not," Claire said. "You look well in it."

"Of course I've always loved hats," her mother said, as if admitting to some secret vice. Claire remembered drawers with felt hats laid into them, and bobbins on the brims of hats, and little aprons of veiling, with spots which, as a child, she thought might crawl over the wearer's face.

"Yes, I remember your hats," Claire said, remembering too the smell of empty perfume bottles and camphor, and a saxe-blue hat that her mother once got on approbation, by post, and wore to Mass before returning it to the shop.

"If you like it, take it," Claire said indulgently.

The mother bought it, along with a reversible raincoat and a pair of shoes. She told the assistant who measured her feet about a pair of shoes which lasted her for seventeen years, and were eventually stolen by a tinker-woman, who afterwards was sent to jail for the theft.

"Poor old creature I wouldn't have wished jail on her," the mother said, and Claire nudged her to shut up. The mother's face flushed under the shelter of her new, wide-brimmed hat.

"Did I say something wrong?" she said as she descended uneasily on the escalator, her parcels held close to her.

"No, I just thought she was busy, it isn't like shops at home," Claire said.

"I think she was enjoying the story," her mother said, gathering courage before she stepped off, on to the ground floor.

At home they prepared the food and the mother tidied the front room before the visitors arrived. Without a word she carried all her own trophies – the tapestry, the pebble picture, the ashtrays, the holy water font and the other ornaments – and put them in the front room alongside the books, the pencil drawings and the poster of Bengal that was a left-over from Claire's dark-skinned lover.

"They're nicer in here," the mother said, apologizing for doing it, and at the same time criticizing the drawing of the nude.

"I'd get rid of some of those things if I were you," she said in a serious tone to her daughter.

Claire kept silent, and sipped the whisky she felt she needed badly. Then to get off the subject she asked after her mother's feet. They were fixing a chiropodist appointment for the next day.

The mother had changed into a blue blouse, Claire into velvet pants, and they sat before the fire on low pouffes with a blue-shaded lamp casting a restful light on their very similar faces.

At sixty, and made-up, the mother still had a poem of a face: round, pale, perfect and with soft eyes, expectant, in spite of what life had brought. On the whites there had appeared blobs of green, the sad green of old age.

"You have a tea-leaf on your eyelid," she said to Claire, putting up her hand to brush it away. It was mascara which got so smeared that Claire had to go upstairs to repair it.

At that precise moment the visitors came.

"They're here," the mother said when the hall bell shrieked.

"Open the door," Claire called down.

"Won't it look odd, if you don't do it?" the mother said.

"Oh, open it," Claire called impatiently. She was quite relieved that they would have to muddle through their own set of introductions.

The dinner went off well. They all liked the food and the mother was not as shy as Claire expected. She told about her journey, but kept the 'mad woman' episode out of it, and about a television programme she'd once seen, showing how bird's nest soup was collected. Only her voice was unnatural.

After dinner Claire gave her guests enormous brandies, because she felt relieved that nothing disastrous had been uttered. Her mother never drank spirits of course.

The fulfilled guests sat back, sniffed brandy, drank their coffee, laughed, tipped their cigarette ash on the floor, having missed the ashtray by a hair's breadth, gossiped, and re-filled their glasses. They smiled at the various new ornaments but did not comment, except to say that the tapestry was nice.

"Claire likes it," the mother said timidly, drawing them into another silence. The evening was punctuated by brief but crushing silences.

"You like Chinese food then?" the husband said. He mentioned a restaurant which she ought to go and see. It was in the East End of London and getting there entailed having a motor car.

"You've been there?" his wife said to the young blonde mistress who had hardly spoken.

"Yes and it was super except for the pork which was drowned in Chanel Number Five. Remember?" she said, turning to the husband, who nodded.

"We must go some time," his wife said. "If ever you can spare an evening." She was staring at the big brandy snifter that she let rock back and forth in her lap. It was for rose petals but when she saw it she insisted on drinking from it. The petals were already dying on the mantelshelf.

"That was the night we found a man against a wall, beaten up," the mistress said, shivering, recalling how she had actually shivered.

"You were so sorry for him," the husband said, amused.

"Wouldn't anyone be?" the wife said tartly, and Claire turned to her mother and promised that they would go to that restaurant the following evening. "We'll see," the mother said. She knew the places she wanted to visit: Buckingham Palace, the Tower of London and the waxworks museum. When she went home it was these places she would discuss with her neighbours who'd already been to London, not some seamy place where men were flung against walls.

"No, not another, it's not good for the baby," the husband said, as his wife balanced her empty glass on the palm of her hand and looked towards the bottle.

"Who's the more important, me or the baby?"

"Don't be silly, Marigold," the husband said.

"Excuse me," she said in a changed voice. "Whose welfare are you thinking about?" She was on the verge of an emotional outburst, her cheeks flushed from brandy and umbrage. By contrast Claire's mother had the appearance of a tombstone, chalk white and deadly still.

"How is the fire?" Claire said, staring at it. On that cue her mother jumped up and sailed off with the coal scuttle.

"I'll get it," Claire said following. The mother did not even wait until they reached the kitchen.

"Tell me," she said, her blue eyes pierced with insult, "which of those two ladies is he married to?"

"It's not your concern," Claire said, hastily. She had meant to smooth it over, to say that the pregnant woman had some mental disturbance, but instead she said hurtful things about her mother being narrow-minded and cruel.

"Show me your friends and I know who you are," the mother said and went away to shovel the coal. She left the filled bucket outside the living-room door and went upstairs. Claire, who had gone back to her guests, heard the mother's footsteps climbing the stairs and going into the bedroom overhead.

"Is your mother gone to bed?" the husband asked.

"She's tired I expect," Claire said, conveying weariness too.

She wanted them to go. She could not confide in them even though they were old friends. They might sneer. They were not friends any more than the ex-lovers, they were all social append-ages, extras, acquaintances cultivated in order to be able to say to other acquaintances, "Well one night a bunch of us went mad and had a nude sit-in . . ." There was no one she trusted, no one she could produce for her mother and feel happy about it.

"Music, brandy, cigarettes . . ." They were recalling her, voicing their needs, wondering who would go to the machine for the cigarettes. Pauline did. They stayed until they'd finished the packet, which was well after midnight.

Claire hurried to her mother's room and found her awake with the light on, fingering her horn rosary beads. The same old black ones.

"I'm sorry," Claire said.

"You turned on me like a tinker," her mother said, in a voice cracked with emotion.

"I didn't mean to," Claire said. She tried to sound reason-able, assured; she tried to tell her mother that the world was a big place and contained many people, all of whom held various views about various things.

"They're not sincere," her mother said, stressing the last word.

"And who is?" Claire said, remembering the treacherous way the lovers vanished, or how former landladies rigged meters so that units of electricity cost double. Her mother had no notion of how lonely it was to read manuscripts all day, and write a poem once in a while, when one became consumed with a memory or an idea, and then to constantly go out, seeking people, hoping that one of them might fit, might know the short-hand of her, body and soul.

"I was a good mother, I did everything I could, and this is all the thanks I get." It was spoken with such justification that Claire turned and laughed, hysterically. An incident leaped to her tongue, something she had never recalled before.

"You went to hospital," she said to her mother, "to have your toe lanced, and you came home and told me, me, that the doctor said, "Raise your right arm until I give you an injection", but when you did, he gave you no injection, he just cut into your toe. Why did you tell it?" The words fell out of her mouth unexpectedly, and she became aware of the awfulness when she felt her knees shaking.

"What are you talking about?" her mother said numbly. The face that was round, in the evening, had become old, twisted, bitter.

"Nothing," Claire said. Impossible to explain. She had violated all the rules: decency, kindness, caution. She would never be able to laugh it off in the morning. Muttering an apology she went to her own room and sat on her bed, trembling. Since her mother's arrival every detail of her childhood kept dogging her. Her present life, her work, the friends she had, seemed insubstantial compared with all that had happened before. She could count the various batches of white, hissing geese – it was geese in those days – that wandered over the swampy fields, one year after another, hid in memory she could locate the pot-holes on the driveway where rain lodged, and where leaking oil from a passing car made rainbows. Looking down into rainbows to escape the colour that was in her mind, or on her tongue. She'd licked four fingers once that were slit by an unexpected razor blade which was wedged upright in a shelf where she'd reached to find a sweet, or to finger the secret dust up there. The same colour had been on her mother's violated toe underneath the big, bulky bandage. In chapel too, the sanctuary light was a bowl of blood with a flame laid into it. These images did not distress her at the time. She used to love to slip into the chapel, alone, in the day-time, moving from one Station of the Cross to the next, being God's exclusive pet, praying that she would die before her mother did, in order to escape being the scapegoat of her father. How could she have known, how could any of them have known that twenty years later, zipped into a heated, plastic tent, treating herself to a steam bath she would suddenly panic and cry out convinced that her sweat became as drops of blood. She put her hands through the flaps and begged the masseuse to protect her, the way she had begged her mother, long ago. Made a fool of herself. The way she made a fool of herself with the various men. The first night she met the Indian she was wearing a white fox collar, and its whiteness under his dark, well-chiselled chin made a stark sight as they walked through a mirrored room to a table, and saw, and were seen in mirrors. He said something she couldn't hear.

"Tell me later," she said, already putting her little claim on him, already saying, "You are not going to abandon me in this room of mirrors, in my bluish-white fox that so compliments your bluish-black lips." But after a few weeks he left, like the others. She was familiar with the various tactics of withdrawal – abrupt, honest, nice. Flowers, notes posted from the provinces, and the 'I don't want you to get hurt' refrain. They reminded her of the trails that slugs leave on a lawn in summer mornings, the sad, silver trails of departure. Their goings were far more vivid than their comings, or was she only capable of remembering the worst? Remembering everything, solving nothing. She undressed, she told herself that her four fingers had healed, that her mother's big toe was now like any other person's big toe, that her father drank tea and held his temper, and that one day she would meet a man whom she loved and did not frighten away. But it was brandy optimism. She'd gone down and carried the bottle up. The brandy gave her hope but it disturbed her heart beats and she was unable to sleep. As morning approached she rehearsed the sweet and conciliatory things she would say to her mother.

They went to Mass on Sunday, but it was obvious that Claire was not in the habit of going: they had to ask the way. Going in, her mother took a small liqueur bottle from her handbag and filled it with holy water from the font.

"It's always good to have it," she said to Claire, but in a bashful way. The outburst had severed them, and they were polite now in a way that should never have been.

After Mass they went – because the mother had stated her wishes – to the waxworks museum, saw the Tower of London and walked across the park that faced Buckingham Palace.

"Very good grazing here," the mother said. Her new shoes were getting spotted from the damp, highish grass. It was raining. The spokes of the mother's umbrella kept tapping Claire's, and no matter how far she drew away, the mother moved accordingly, to prong her, it seemed.

"You know," the mother said. "I was thinking."

Claire knew what was coming. Her mother wanted to go home; she was worried about her husband, her fowls, the washing that would have piled up, the spring wheat that would have to be sown. In reality she was miserable. She and her daughter were farther away now than when they wrote letters each week and discussed the weather, or work, or the colds they'd had.

"You're only here six days," Claire said, "And I want to take you to the theatre and restaurants. Don't go."

"I'll think about it," the mother said. But her mind was made up.

Two evenings later they waited in the airport lounge, hesitant to speak, for fear they might miss the flight number.

"The change did you good," Claire said. Her mother was togged out in new clothes and looked smarter. She had two more new hats in her hand, carrying them in the hope they would escape the notice of the customs men.

"I'll let you know if I have to pay duty on them," she said.

"Do," Claire said, smiling, straightening her mother's collar, wanting to say something endearing, something that would atone, without having to go over their differences, word for word.

"No one can say but that you fitted me out well, look at all my style," the mother said smiling at her image in the glass door of the telephone box. "And our trip up the river," she said. "I think I enjoyed it more than anything." She was referring to a short trip they'd taken down the Thames to Westminister. They had planned to go in the opposite direction towards the greenness of Kew and Hampton Court but they'd left it – at least Claire had left it – too late and could only go towards the city on a passenger boat that was returning from those green places.

Claire had been miserly with her time and on that particular evening she'd sat at her desk pretending to work, postponing the time until she got up and rejoined her mother, who was downstairs sewing on all the buttons that had fallen off over the years. And now the mother was thanking her, saying it had been lovely. Lovely. They had passed warehouses and cranes brought to their evening standstill yellow and tilted, pylons like floodlit honeycombs in the sky, and boats, and gasworks, and filthy chimneys. The spring evening had been drenched with sewerage smell and yet her mother went on being thankful.

"I hope my mad lady won't be aboard," the mother said, trying to make a joke out of it now.

"Not likely," Claire said, but the mother declared that life was full of strange and sad coincidences. They looked at each other, looked away, criticized a man who was wolfing sandwiches from his pocket, looked at the airport clock and compared the time on their watches.

"Sssh . . . sssh . . ." Claire had to say.

"That's it," they both said then, relieved. As if they had secretly feared the flight number would never be called.

At the barrier they kissed, their damp cheeks touched and stayed for a second like that, each registering the other's sorrow.

"I'll write to you. I'll write oftener," Claire said, and for a few minutes she stood there waving, weeping, not aware that the visit was over and that she could go back to her own life now, such as it was.

Colleen Antonia Patterson

We Rarely Touched at All

we rarely touched at all.
once i met her at heathrow
saw this small grey-haired
woman glancing anxiously
around, raised my newspaper
to catch her glance, walked
quickly to the exit. we
hugged briefly, she swallowed
several times trying to stop
the tears. i relieved her
of her luggage, guided her to
the working bus.
she is my mother and she lets
me do things for her.

she believed in my strength
later she found that i am
not strong. still, now,
she lets me carry her luggage
and track down the right trains
and order the drinks and would
never suggest that i am anything
but strong except she rarely
speaks of her pain to me.

Sheila Rowbotham

My Friend

My friend
cooks sweet
apples
far into
the night.

A gift
of gentleness
through time,
country kitchens
in the sun
perfume
the dark
still.

Their fragrance
lingers
until
light.

Vera Brittain

Testament of Friendship

Those years with Winifred taught me that the type of friendship which reaches its apotheosis in the story of David and Jonathan is not a monopoly of the masculine sex. Hitherto, perhaps owing to a lack of women recorders, this fact has been found difficult to accept by men, and even by other women. Some feminine individualists believe that they flatter men by fostering the fiction of women's jealous inability to love and respect one another. Other sceptics are roused by any record of affection between women to suspicions habitual among the over-sophisticated.

"Too, *too* Chelsea!" Winifred would comment amiably in after years when some zealous friend related the newest legend current about us in the neigbourhood.

After a year or two of constant companionship, our response to each other's needs and emotions had become so instinctive that in our correspondence one of us often replied to some statement or request made by the other before the letter which contained it had arrived. When I wrote Winifred from America at the beginning of May 1927 that I thought I was going to have a child, she replied that during the previous week she remembered having an unusually vivid dream about a baby of mine. She called it "the beloved and lovely child" – a sentiment which she always felt for my son John Edward from the time that he was born at the end of that year.

The only personal experience of telepathy that I have ever known occurred in connection with Winifred. One day in 1923, when I was out of London on a periodic teaching expedition, a class was cancelled and I arrived back at our Doughty Street flat before tea-time instead of the usual supper-time. Not knowing that Winifred was out, I ran up the stairs and called gaily, "Hullo, my dear!" as I opened the door.

Shortly before supper Winifred returned from an after-noon's shopping in the West End. As soon as she saw me she inquired rather oddly: "Look here – did you come back to-day at the usual time?"

I explained that I had been early, and she then asked:

"Well, did you go straight to the flat?"

"Yes," I replied. "I came on the bus from London Bridge as usual. Why do you ask?"

"Because," she said, "I had the queerest experience this afternoon. I was in Berkeley Street, going to Piccadilly, and suddenly I heard your voice just behind me calling, 'Hullo, my dear!' I turned round quite startled – and found you weren't there."

"When exactly did that happen?" I asked.

"It was just about four o'clock," she said.

I then told her that precisely at that hour I had run up the stairs and called my greeting to the empty flat.

Passionately as I desired Winifred's friendship, deeply as I needed it with the starving need of an individual whose earlier loves had been prematurely and violently shattered, the building of it was her achievement rather than mine. In the years which followed the War I was not easy to live with, and I often wondered even then why Winifred showed no sign of wanting to leave me. The heredity inconsiderately bequeathed me by nervous irritable ancestors, combined with the loss of every person for whose life I feared during the War, had implanted a habit of apprehension which I now accept as a life-long burden, since twenty years have not sufficed to remove it. To-day I can conceal and sometimes forget it, but in the nineteen-twenties it was perpetual and acute. Every hour of suspense, however slight its cause, meant unmitigated agony. Every minor set-back, criticism or disappointment upset me at least twice as much as any sane person. Our stimulating life in London, with its constant surprises and excitements, was probably the worst that I could then have lived, for whenever we spent a country holiday together at Whipsnade or Cornwall or Burgh Heath, the sense of strain began to disappear. But that London life was inevitable if a beginning was ever to be made with the writer's career that I had already postponed for seven interminable years, and Winifred, realizing this, resolved that since the surroundings could not be changed the companion chosen must act as compensation.

Her own capacity for swift exasperation was not negligible; I once saw her take an inefficient secretary, who had bungled

147

an important telephone message, firmly by the shoulders and shake her like a child. But it was chiefly fools whom she would not suffer; provided that intelligence and goodwill existed, she was ready to forgive every accompanying disadvantage. With me her generosity and forbearance were unfailing; patiently she consoled my lunatic anxiety over adverse reviews, rejected manuscripts, family ailments, and other minor everyday annoyances which to her must have seemed absurdly trivial. Sometimes, ruefully seeing myself as others saw me, I asked her half sadly and half amusedly why she put up with it. She would then answer quite seriously that she was a debtor to life, and therefore felt under an obligation to repay with love and service a friend whose personal history had given less reason for gaiety and confidence than her own.

Gillian Tindall

The Visitor

"Sit down, dear, do sit down, you must be tired coming all the way up here. Haven't you brought your – your machine with you, though? . . . Yes, you know what I mean surely? I thought you'd bring it. The last person that came from the wireless did. No, television – that's what he came from, but it's all the same isn't it? . . . I'll remember what the machine's called in a minute. It's on the tip of my tongue.

I'll get you a nice cup of tea. Oh yes I will, dear, you can't say No, I always get my visitors a cup of tea, no trouble at all, I've got everything ready. What I say is, if you're lucky enough to have the use of your legs at nearly ninety-three you ought to use them oughtn't you? No use just sitting around letting others wait on you. I wasn't brought up to it, anyway.

A tape-recorder! That's what it's called. Where's your tape-recorder? . . . That's it? You don't say. Gracious. Things get smaller and smaller, don't they, I thought it was your handbag. Well that must make things a lot easier for you, dear. I was thinking, there now, there's this poor young girl coming all the way out here on the Central Line with a heavy machine to carry, I do hope she'll manage, girls aren't as strong today as when I was a girl . . . Oh in a car. I see. Of course I never learnt to drive. I would have liked to, I think – my father was a coachman, you know, and owned his own cab later – but I daresay that if I'd become used to driving everywhere like you young people I shouldn't have the strong legs I still have now, should I?

. . . There we are, dear, everything's on the tray I think. Do you take sugar? No, I didn't think you would – you young people are always thinking of your figures – but I put it on the tray just in case. I don't take it myself – haven't since I was seventy-five. Doctor's orders. Yes, sugar diabetes. Tiresome, isn't it, but Nurse looks in twice a day now to give me my jabs. Of course, as I told her, I could perfectly well give them to

149

myself – did for years – but I think she likes to do it herself, makes her feel useful. Poor thing, she'd had a sad life I believe; her only daughter's in Australia, she told me, and she's not a woman with much *courage* for life, if you take my meaning – a bit of a moaner . . . She thinks too much. Yes. Well, anyway – you've got to have something, haven't you? When you're nearly ninety-three, I mean.

Do have a biscuit – if your diet allows it . . . Oh, you don't diet? Well isn't that nice! Now I want you to tell me something about yourself . . . You've come to interview *me*? Yes, I know dear, but it's a bit of nonsense, isn't it? I mean – what can I tell you that could interest people. I'm too old, dear. Once, now, I could have told you all sorts of things. Oh I had quite a lot of opinions in my time. Little-Miss-Knowall my mother used to call me. And at one time I gave talks to the Townswomen's Guilds on making Patchwork for Victory. In the War that was. Not the one my sons were in, of course, but the second one . . . But I really don't think much about talking these days, dear.

The patchwork, you said? Oh yes. Patchwork. Yes I used to do a lot of patchwork once. We'd always done it at home, see – Mother and me and my sisters. All the bed covers and that, and for the Queen's Jubilee – Queen Victoria that would be, dear, you wouldn't remember her of course – Mother and Lily – that was my youngest sister – made a lovely cushion cover all in applicky work with God Bless Our Queen on it . . . No, I didn't work on it myself. I was grown up by that time and out in service with a family in Brondesbury. Yes, seventeen I was then – quick at figures, aren't you dear! I've always been quick at figures myself. Anyway I was busy sewing my trousseau then – on my afternoon's off, you know – because the next year I got married . . . No, I don't recall the date. Sometime in the July, it was, because that was when Bert – he was my husband – had a week off. He was in the ironmongery business – travelling he was then. A good job really . . . No I've never set much store by dates. After all, one day's much less another, isn't it, when you come down to it; it's only thinking it's a special day that makes it something. An anniversary doesn't mean anything to my way of thinking . . . And anyway there's only one date that should mean anything to me now isn't there, and I don't know when that is.

. . . Can't you guess what date I mean? . . . Well never mind dear, that's just my little joke. I'll tell you by and by.

... Oh, you were interested in the patchwork ... What? No, no I've not got that cushion now. No, I've no idea where it is, nor all those bed covers neither. Torn up for dusters long ago, I reckon ... A shame, you think? Well I don't know. What's past using, is past using, isn't it? We never set much store by them ourselves anyway ... Yes I did hear that some of that sort of stuff fetches high prices now. The other person from the wireless told me actually – from the television. I mean. The young man who came before. He went on about how valuable those quilts would have been today. Can't see it myself. If you want the honest truth, dear, I think people are a bit sentimental today – you know: soft. No offence meant dear, of course – and none taken, I hope?

If you're really interested there's a few little pieces in that bureau drawer there – yes, go ahead, have a look, I've no secrets there! Just bits they are. Bits I did years ago when I was first married and then later I used them as examples – for my talk to the Guilds, you know. I never made them into anything and it seems a bit late now, doesn't it?

Yes dear. I know some of 'em have still got their backing papers on them. 'Templates' you call those – they're for keeping the patches in shape while you sew them in. Oh I used to cut the templates from any old paper – anything that was nice and stiff that was. Let's see ... Yes, that's a bit of a laundry list, isn't it ... Don't know where those come from, can't read that tiny print well these days – they look like a Temperance tract or something, don't they? ... Oh I forget, you wouldn't know about them, would you dear? In these days it's all sex isn't it, in the papers and that? Well in those days it was all religion and temperance. The one thing's as daft as the other, if you ask me. Just crazes – you know what I mean?

... That's a bit of my sister Dora's writing, can't see what. Must've been a letter from her I cut up. She didn't write no more after a while though. She was the one who went to Canada. Her husband was in the food business – great fat thing he was, too.

... Yes, that looks like a bit from a child's copybook, doesn't it? Nice thick paper them writing books from the Board School were, I used quite a lot of that ... Yes, dear, a child learning to write. Yes, you can see the words, can't you?

... Oh I don't know dear. It might have been Jim's or there again it might have been Bill's. I really don't remember, dear.

It doesn't signify, does it? – They've both been dead and gone so long.

Yes, Jim was my older boy . . . He was sent to the Front when he was eighteen and he Went almost at once. Bill was a year younger. He would have been nineteen when the War ended but he Went just before the Armistice. No dear, like I said, I don't recall the exact dates. And I didn't keep the telegrams or nothing. It's a very long time ago now, dear, anyway. And you get over things, you see. In the end.

Look – you know the 'In Memorials' people like to put in the newspaper? Well years ago there used to be ever such a lot from the War – a whole column of them on some dates, all those lads who went west on the Somme or in the other big battles. But there aren't today. You try looking in the paper regularly and you'll hardly see any from that War now – well maybe one or two now and again, but hardly any. Well I mean, that just proves it, doesn't it? Nothing lasts forever, not even that. It all gets worn away in the end, dear, all the feeling, just like the old quilts.

No, we didn't have no more children after those two. We were building up the business, see. We had this shop out Hendon way. It's all houses there now, but it was like the country then. We used to stock all sorts of things for the farms. Bill hooks and plough shares and that. I bet you've never seen ploughing done with horses, have you? . . . Oh, I see – abroad. Oh well, I wouldn't know about that. I wouldn't have minded going abroad, mind you, they say it's an interesting experience – but I'm a bit too old for them now. Experiences, I mean. Yes. Ninety-three next birthday. My mother was only seventy when she Went. But of course they had a hard life in those days – and they were ignorant too. I had a good education myself. I was always top of the class though I say it myself. I sometimes think that's why I'm not sentimental, like some people are.

Yes, put those bits and pieces away again for me, would you dear. Don't know why I keep them, really, but as they've been there so long they might as well stay. You never know – my next visitor might be interested. Oh yes, I get a lot of visitors. I'm lucky that way. Mrs Lewisohn – she's the lady that runs the Welfare, quite young she is, about fifty I suppose – she says I'm quite spoiled! But what I really think, dear, is that people like to visit me because I keep up with the times. I mean – I don't dwell on. the past, do I?

. . . You think your listeners would like it if I did! Goodness gracious. Well, you can't please everyone, that's what I always say. I'm afraid you'll have to make do with what you've got dear. Perhaps you'll come and see me again some time? There's always my hundredth birthday to look forward to isn't there! Unless that other date I mentioned comes up first.

It may well. I mean, I can't expect to go on living forever at my age, can I?

I think about that a lot. Most of the time, in fact. I think that these old people who just think about their next meal and what Nurse said are silly, don't you? I mean, we've all got to Go, haven't we? No sense in running away from it.

Just one thing, dear, before you go; how are you going to announce me? I mean, would it be 'Mrs Soames' or – ? . . . Well most people do call me Mrs Soames, yes, they have done for a long time. It's like that, you know, when everyone's younger than you . . . But what I wanted to say was, my name's Mary. Mary Soames. If you should want to call me by my full name, I mean.

. . . Yes. Yes I'd like that. No one's called me Mary for – oh, must be twenty years now. It'd make a nice change.

Well I expect you've guessed what that other date is? Must keep it in mind, mustn't I, even though I don't know when it'll be! No sense in running away from it . . .

. . . No. No, I'm not frightened of dying. Of course not. Never have been. What a peculiar idea. You'll have to get out of those sorts of fancies you know, dear, they won't do you any good. As you get older yourself, I mean.

. . . There is just one thing that does worry me a bit. Shall I tell you? Well. Like I said, I'm very lucky to have a lot of visitors out here. And most of them have been sent by Mrs Lewisohn or have come like yourself from the television, so I know that's alright. But . . . well, the other day this young man called . . .

. . . I don't know where he was from. If I did, I wouldn't worry, would I? He did tell me but there was a car making a noise in the street and I didn't catch what he said. Why should he come to my door? I keep wondering.

. . . No, no not a thug, I should say, nor a spiv . . . Quite quiet spoken, really, and gentlemanly, only with the long hair like they have today and one of those coats that look like a hearth-rug turned back to front. They call them hippies, don't they? That's what Nurse said when I told her. But he was very polite and didn't want money or nothing . . .

He just said he'd come to pay me a little visit. Gave me a bit of a turn, it did.

. . . Well, I mean it was the way he said it. As if he knew I'd been waiting for him.

. . . Well of course I hadn't really, because I wasn't expecting him, was I? But he acted somehow as if I was. As if we'd had a date with one another.

He was very nice, I can't complain about anything . . . But he said he'd be back.

I keep wondering when."

Judith Pasternak

My Bloom Will Never Fade

For My Grandmother

Each morning the palsied old man
Carries his blind wife to her chair
And back to bed each evening.

She doesn't know him,
Nor the nurse who feeds her
The unseen food his trembling hand
                              can't aim.

As helpless and unconscious now
As the nursling eighty years ago
Whose mother dreamed of half her baby's future:

To become beautiful
To love and be loved by handsome men
To bear a beautiful daughter
To grow strawberries for her grandchildren
To hang on the wall the matriarchal picture –
        Herself, still vigorous, her daughter,
        The daughter's daughters and their children –

To see her man lose stature
To see him start to tremble
To find gaps in her memory
To find herself, one day, too weak to walk
To see the light grow dim

And the old man wonders
As he lifts her from her chair
Whether she thinks herself a helpless babe again
And him her mother
And she herself with so much still ahead.

Marge Piercy

Sign

The first white hair coils in my hand,
more wire than down or feather.
Out of the bathroom mirror it glittered at me.
I plucked it, feeling thirty creep in my joints,
and found it silver. It does not melt.

My twentieth birthday lean as glass
spring vacation I stayed in the college town
twanging misery's electric banjo offkey.
I wanted to inject love right into the veins
of my thigh and wake up visible:
to vibrate color
like the minerals in stones under black light.
My best friend went home without loaning me money.
Hunger was all of the time the taste of my mouth.

Now I am ripened and sag a little from my spine.
More than most I have been the same ragged self
in all colors of luck dripping and dry,
yet love has nested in me and gradually eaten
those sense organs I used to feel with.
I have eaten my hunger soft and my ghost grows stronger.

Living in the sun so long my bones are tanned,
I am glad with my love, but everything counts now
and is counted. Gradually I am turning
to chalk, to humus, to pages and pages of paper,
to fine silver wire like something a violin
could be strung with, or somebody strung up,
or current run through: silver truly,
this hair, shiny and purposeful as forceps
if I knew how to use it.

A Sequence of Photographs

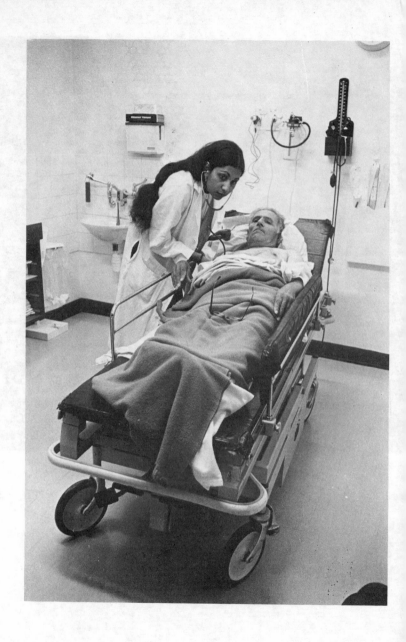

Miss Nicola Jane Florence

This piece of writing would be called 'child's hand-writing' were it not a fact. It was written by an old lady with uneven pen-strokes now and trembling in later lines and corners that suffered in its unsteadiness and incoherence as she thought through its turns and twists. After some difficulties, Miss Alice wanted very hard to get this one line right to a mother.

The Coming of Autumn Red

The spirit of the Silumkon is laden with the Winster — this is quite so in Frontise, and then comes just but the Winster sprinkled field, but by the universal sort, the way

Points for Discussion and Suggestions for Writing

(Suggestions for writing are marked with an asterisk.)

The Butterfly Frolic

1 "I see what you mean." Joan's mother had warned Miss Flegg that there was a problem with the Butterfly frolic. In pairs, discuss and then act out the conversation between the two women which leads to Joan becoming a mothball in the show.

2 Joan thinks her mother betrayed her. Do you agree? Discuss what she did and why – was it really a betrayal?

* 3 "Besides, who would think of marrying a mothball? A question my mother put to me often, later, in other forms." What does this mean? Write out a conversation between Joan and her mother when Joan was ten years older in which her mother asks that question again in another form.

Miss Kindergarten America

4 This piece of writing could be called satire. It takes a basic idea, e.g. girls are conditioned into being too concerned with their appearance, and exaggerates it until it is ridiculous and comic. Go through the article carefully and take notes about what the author is really telling us. What are the main problems Miss Kindergarten America faces? Which ones face girls in real life?

The Coming of Maureen Peal

5 This story is about a situation we have all either witnessed or been involved in. From the outside it could just look like a childish squabble, but for those involved it can be very

painful. Use your own experience of primary-school rows to write a story called "A Childish Squabble".

6 Discuss the story. Use these questions to start you off. Exactly why did the sisters hate Maureen? Read the beginning of the story carefully to find all the reasons they give. Later on in the story they began to soften towards her. How do you explain the change?
Maureen protects Pecola from the bullying of the boys. How did she manage to rescue her? Why did she do it? Think about the end of the story as well as the time she actually rescues Pecola.
What is your final impression of Maureen?

7 At the end of the story, the girls are left "sinking under the wisdom, accuracy and relevance of Maureen's last words". Discuss what the author means by this. What do you think the girls really learned from what Maureen said?

The Kiss

8 This story takes a "romantic situation", the first kiss, but it treats it in a very down-to-earth way. Collect some cartoon strip stories from girls' magazines and compare the way they present the lead-up to the big moment – the kiss – with the way this story tackles the situation. Which do you think is most realistic? Why do you think magazines have so many romantic stories? What messages do they carry about how boys and girls should behave?

* 9 Look at the story from a different point of view. What was Bill thinking and feeling? Write your own version of Bill's story using the same information but using him as the central character.

Daffodils

10 "'Miss Murcheson has never really *lived*,' said Doris." Discuss why the girls felt like this about their teacher. Were they right?

*11 Women like Miss Murcheson are often described as spinsters or "on the shelf". Why do you think society, like the girls, undervalues their lives? Write an essay in which you discuss this problem.

A Telephone Call

12 This story uses the rhythm of a person speaking. Try reading a section out loud in pairs. Discuss how Dorothy Parker achieves this effect. What techniques does she use?

*13 Try the technique for yourself. Write a short monologue entitled "The date" in which you describe the reactions of someone, male or female, waiting for a date who doesn't turn up.

14 The woman waiting for her telephone call talks mainly about a particular man, but every now and then "he" becomes "they". "He couldn't have minded my calling him up. I know you shouldn't keep telephoning them. I know they don't like that." She seems to have a list of rules about what "they don't like". Read through the passage and work out her "rules". What do you think of them? How do you think she learned them?

Reclamation

15 This story is placed after "The Telephone Call" because it shows a woman fighting back. Compare the two stories. What do the women have in common? How do they differ in the way they "respond" to the things that happen to them in life.

*16 Imagine that you were explaining this story to someone in another class who hadn't discussed it and worked out its meaning. Write a brief explanation which would help her or him understand it.

17 In between the two stories there is a group of poems in which women discuss various aspects of being in love. They have all been chosen because they avoid clichés and stereotypes. Read them and discuss your reactions to them.

Sarah

*18 Retell the story in another form. Either write a poem, possibly a ballad, called "Sarah's story", or write a newspaper account of the event.

19 Who do you think wrote the letter claiming that Oliver was the father of the baby? Why was the letter written? Discuss this carefully.

20 Why was Sarah thrown out and left to die with this last baby when she'd already had others? Why did she have to suffer and not the father? Does this kind of double standard still exist? Discuss what you know from your own experience about the "rules" for men and women. Go on to read (or sing!) the song which follows. Discuss what it has to say about double standards.

The Diary of a Farmer's Wife

21 Anne Hughes kept a diary for a year between 1796–1797. It's an account of the everyday life of a farmer's wife. The section you've read gives you some insight into the social life of the community. The diary captures a way of life that has long since vanished. Discuss the passage. What do you learn about that way of life?

22 Most of the history you read is written by and about men. Do you agree? Do a little research in your school or local library. How many female writers can you find? What about the subjects? Dip into the books and see whether women's lives are described as often as men's lives. Discuss the findings of your research.

Hymeneal

23 Susan thought she knew what she was doing when she married Jesse. Discuss what you think will be the difference between her assumptions and reality.

*24 Susan will probably not want to admit to her mother that life with Jesse is not exactly as she'd hoped, but she might tell a close friend. Write two letters, one to her mother and one to a friend in which Susan reflects on her life a year after her marriage.

Weekend

25 Why doesn't Martha leave Martin? Discuss why she tolerated this marriage.

*26 Imagine Martha can't hold back her anger and finally rows with Martin. Write the scene in which she tells him what she thinks of him. How does he react?

27 Think about the ending. Discuss it carefully. What does it mean? Why did Fay Weldon choose to end the story in this way?

*28 This story is about a middle-class family. Do you think working-class families have similar tensions? Try writing about a weekend in a working-class family. What kind of role does the wife/mother play?

*29 Look again at the story. Can you draw up an agreement between Martha and Martin which would help them share the jobs in the family?

Louisa

30 Was Louisa right to risk the security of her family by not marrying Nye? Discuss the problem which faced her. Would you have made the same decision?

*31 When Louisa returned from her uncle's house, she finds her problem solved. Write an alternative ending to the story.

*32 On Louisa's exhausting walk home, she must have felt that all was lost. Write a poem which expresses her feelings.

Désirée's Baby

33 The story is set in the deep south of America at the end of the last century. Discuss what you have learned from it about attitudes to race in that society.

*34 "A letter to my dead wife". Write Armand's letter to Désirée in which he reveals the contents of his mother's letter and tries to tell his dead wife about his feelings on reading it.

A Proper Marriage

*35   Use the vivid description of birth in this passage to help you write a poem on the topic.

36   Women are now demanding much more say in how they give birth. Some people say they should make the final decision about the drugs they are given to control the pain, the position they adopt to give birth (the position we take for granted with the women lying on her back may not always be the best), and about the many devices used to monitor the baby's progress. Discuss the issues involved. Do the doctors have more rights than the mothers? What is the role of the father? What do you think is best for the baby? You could do some research on this. There are many books on the topic because it is so controversial.

37   Look at the people described in the passage. Martha got support from some of them and not others. Who helped her and how?

38   Think about the whole passage. What makes it such a powerful piece of writing? Try to identify some features of the writing which help build the scene and give you insight into the experience.

Cords

39   What are the cords which hold mother and daughter together?

*40   Write a letter from Claire's mother to her father. It should tell him all the news from London and remind him of things to do back home. It should also explain the mother's reaction to Claire's life-style.

41   Is it inevitable that mothers and daughters should grow apart like this? What do you think has separated Claire and her mother? Do you think similar things separate other mothers and daughters?

42   Claire begins to realize how close she is to her mother. Do you think, as time goes on, she will come even closer?

43 Look at the poem which follows this story. "We Rarely Touched At All". What similarities can you find between the story and the poem? What do you think is most effective?

Testament of Friendship

44 You don't often read about true friendship between women, as the opening paragraph of this passage points out. Why do you think this is so?

45 Both women were deeply affected by events in the First World War. Both were starting careers as writers and political campaigners. How did they support each other? Read the passage carefully and discuss it.

*46 The poem "My Friend" which comes before this passage is on the same theme. Use it and the passage to help you write a story or a poem about friendship.

The Visitor

47 "What can I tell you that could interest people. I'm too old, dear." What does Mary Soames have to say that would interest people?

48 There are two unanswered questions in the story: what is the date she is waiting for and who was the "hippie" visitor? What do you think the answers are?

49 Read the two poems which accompany this story. What do you learn from them about old age? Which do you prefer?

*50 "Three score years and ten" – write about what you imagine you will be like when you're old.

Acknowledgements

We are grateful to the following for permission to reproduce copyright material:

Associated Book Publishers Ltd for poem 'Lady in Red' from *For Colored Girls Who Have Considered Suicide When the Rainbow is Enuf* by Ntozake Shange, pub. Methuen London; Chatto & Windus Ltd for 'The Coming of Maureen Peal' from *The Bluest Eyes* by Toni Morrison; Chatto & Windus Ltd & the author for an extract from the chapter 'Winter' pp 47–58 *The Bluest Eye* by Toni Morrison; Constable & Co Ltd for 'Sarah' from *The Stories of Mary Lavin* Vol II; André Deutsch Ltd for an extract from *Lady Oracle* by Margaret Attwood; the author's agents for an extract from *Hymeneal* by Janice Elliot; the Essex Music Group and Stormking Music Inc for the song 'I'm Gonna be an Engineer' by Peggy Seeger, used by permission of Harmony Music Ltd; Granada Publishing for an extract from *A Proper Marriage* by Doris Lessing; Hodder & Stoughton Ltd for an extract from *Weekend – Watching Me Watching You* by Fay Weldon; Little, Brown & Co for poem 'I Wrung My Hands. . .' from *Poems of Akhmatova* trans. Kunitz & Hayward © 1973 by Stanley Kunitz & Max Hayward this poem first appeared in *VOGUE*; the author's agents for the story 'The Cords' by Edna O'Brien from *The Love Object* pub. Jonathan Cape Ltd; Onlywomen Press, the Literary Executor for the late Colleen Antonia Patterson and the authors for the poems 'My Friend' by Sheila Rowbotham, 'I am being born' by Aspen, 'We Rarely Touched At All' by Colleen Patterson and 'when you accuse me' by Patricia Van Twest, all first publ. in *One Foot on The Mountain; an anthology of British Feminist Poetry 1969–1979* ed. Lilian Mohin; author's agents for story 'A Telephone Call' by Dorothy Parker from *The Collected Dorothy Parker* pub. Gerald Duckworth & Co Ltd 1973; the author, Judith Pasternak for her poem 'My Bloom Will Never Fade' from *Stories from Women's Lives* pub. More Than Half the World Press, copyright Judith Pasternak 1979; Penguin Books Ltd for an extract from pp. 70–81 *The Diary of a Farmer's Wife* by Anne Hughes 1981, © Mollie Preston, 1937, 1964, 1980; the author, Christine Purkis for an extract from her story *The Kiss*; the author, Julie Sapsford for her poem 'While Walking on a Wire Tightrope'; Saturday Review Magazine Co for extract 'Miss Kindergarten America' from 'Phoenix Nest' *Saturday Review* © 1964; Sidgwick & Jackson Ltd for an extract from *Daffodils* by Elizabeth Bowen; the author's agents for story 'The Visitor' from *Dances of Death* by Gillian Tindall, copyright Gillian Tindall 1973; Virago Press for an extract from pp. 117–120 *A Testament of Friendship* by Vera Brittain, © the Literary Executors of Vera Brittain 1940; Wesleyan University Press for poem 'Sign' from *Breaking Camp* by Marge Piercy, Copyright © 1968 by Marge Piercy, poem first appeared in *Shenandoah*.

Whilst every effort has been made, we are unable to trace the copyright holders of the story 'Reclamation' from *Lives and Stories* by Glenda Adams and would appreciate any information which would enable us to do so.

We are grateful to the Toledo Museum of Art, Ohio, for permission to reproduce on the cover the painting by Cecilia Beaux, American 1855–1942, entitled *After the Meeting*, 1914, oil on canvas (104 × 71.5 cm) gift of Florence Scott Libbey; to Zabriskie Editions, page i; and to Sally and Richard Greenhill for 19 photographs from their collection.

Longman Imprint Books
General Editor: Michael Marland CBE MA

*Cassette available

182